Monika's Blues

On the Trail of the German Harmonica
and
African-American Blues Culture

Herbert Quelle

Monika's Blues
by Herbert Quelle

ISBN: 978-1-880788-27-1

Cover design by
Kevin Spitta
Based on an idea by Herbert Quelle

Cover photo of Billy Branch
taken by Herbert Quelle

Author photo by
Paul Crisanti

First Edition, 2017
..

NCSA Literatur
401 East Michigan Street
Indianapolis, IN 46204

NCSA Literatur is the publishing arm of the *Indiana German Heritage Society* and the *Max Kade Center for German-American Studies* at IUPUI.

Table of Content

"There is no exact person, time or location which actually gave birth to the Blues. Certainly, we did not leap off slave ships and onto the auction block playing harmonicas and doing the jitterbug! The souls of Black folks have innate characteristics, and Blues is a manifestation of those affected by certain conditions."

Lincoln T. Beauchamp (Chicago Beau)

Foreword
by
Billy Branch

Since the age of eleven, I have never been without the possession of a harmonica. It was at that age, that I walked into a Woolworth's department store and saw a shiny metal harmonica encased in a glass display case. I had never seen or heard anyone play a harmonica, but a little voice inside me told me that I could play it. I asked the clerk the price. After paying the clerk the dollar, I deftly opened the slide styled box of the Valencia harmonica (a German folk style instrument). I carefully removed the harmonica and placed it in my mouth. Astonishingly, as I had intuitively known, I immediately was able to play simple folk tunes such as *Oh Susanna*, *Mary Had a Little Lamb*, and Christmas carols such as *Jingle Bells* and *Silent Night*. I quickly became aware that I was able to play practically any folk melody that I could think of.

One can easily understand why *Monika's Blues* has a special significance to me. This is an unconventional story about an unconventional instrument. The serendipitous sequence of events that occur within this story might seem incredible, if not for the fact that my own sojourn is just as amazing, if not more so. It was a mere six years later as a soon to be freshman entering the University of Illinois at Chicago that I found myself witnessing the greatest Blues festival in history. The "Bringing the Blues Back Home Festival" occurred on August 30, 1969 in Grant Park, downtown Chicago. Muddy Waters, Big Mama Thornton, Buddy Guy, Jr. Wells, Little Milton, Sleepy John Estes, James Cotton, Betty Everett, Robert Jr. Lockwood, The Aces, Johnny Littlejohn, Big Walter Horton and Koko Taylor were just a few of the almost fifty legends who performed on that life-changing day. The festival was produced by Willie Dixon and Murphy Dunne (the son of one of Mayor J. Daley's top political allies) who provided the backup band of his Chicago Blues All Stars. This was the first time that I'd ever heard live blues.

Seven years later, unbelievably, I became the harp player for Willie Dixon's Chicago Blues All-Stars. It is noteworthy to mention that just like Luther, one of the pivotal characters in the novel, I also at the age of seventeen, ignorantly did not like, understand, or have any desire to listen to or learn about the Blues. Looking back, I have come to understand that it was destiny that led me into that Woolworths store to prepare me for that fateful day. I have been a faithful devotee and ardent practitioner ever since.

The author has taken us on a surreal journey laden

with facts and history about the instrument and a plethora of background information about the blues harp and its respective players. The irony of a German manufactured instrument finding its way into the hands and mouths of itinerant southern African-American bluesmen is a much emphasized theme throughout the narrator's almost magical adventure. Although it is true that this book will be of extreme interest to harmonica players or "harpers" as the term the author prefers, it will also pique the interest of the casual blues lover, or anyone even slightly interested in the history of the harmonica and its subsequent emergence as one of the dominant instruments in the blues. Although set as a fictional novel, the story is laden with a multitude of significant historical facts about the harmonica and its respective players, replete with interesting and entertaining anecdotes. One begins to wonder how much of the story is indeed fiction.

However, it is obvious that the author did an exhaustive amount of research, providing statistical sales and exportation information of the "people's instrument" principally by the German Hohner Corporation. It is astounding to learn that hundreds of millions of harmonicas found their way to American soil, in a relatively short span of time. Although Hohner had become by far the dominant brand, and harp of choice for all, we learn that there were many other German manufacturers in times past. Of these, only Seydel and Hohner are currently still active. It is noteworthy to mention that currently brands such as Suzuki Manji (my harp of choice) and Lee Oskar harmonicas are now also very popular in the blues field.

Throughout the author's quest to chronicle the timeline of the appearance and usage of the harmonica on United States soil, we are constantly reminded of the trials and tribulations of the African American experience. One cannot effectively discuss the Blues as historical legacy without acknowledging slavery, Jim Crow segregation, discrimination and their respective atrocities. Although *Monika's Blues* does not make these themes the central focus of the novel, it wisely, nonetheless, does not avoid them. After all, the Blues according to Willie Dixon is "The Facts of Life." For southern (as well as northern) Blacks, racial discrimination was a daily fact of life.

Take a ride in a Volkswagen Beetle (one of many ironic metaphors) set your course for the Mississippi Blues trail. Be prepared to meet interesting and friendly angels along the way. Expect a thoroughly entertaining education by "Monika" and her Blues. You will not be disappointed.

Billy Branch

2016

Billy Branch is a three time Grammy nominee and an Emmy Award winner who had the unique privilege of being taught by Big Walter Horton, Carey Bell, Junior Wells, and James Cotton. In addition to international touring for more than 35 years, Billy has been sharing the history of the Blues around the world in his highly acclaimed Blues in Schools Program since 1978.

Preface

There is general consensus that the Blues is a major genuine African-American contribution to the culture of the United States of America. From the 1950s on it found a growing fan base in Europe. Without its influence, beat and rock music in Europe would not have developed as they did. I believe the Blues deserves recognition as belonging to the World Musical Heritage, if one ever formally establishes such a concept.

Further, there is no doubt that the major export market for the German manufactured harmonica since the 1870s was the United States. The instrument was cheap and readily available for everybody at department stores and small music shops as well as through mail order companies. Its contribution to the popular success of the Blues has been underrated and is under researched.

There is finally broad agreement that in the 1930s the reputation of the harmonica began to change. It was seen less as a toy, and finally accepted as a serious instrument. The great number and appreciation of harmonica orchestras in the United States may have been both a cause for and an effect of this development. The importance of the harmonica in various musical genres including the Blues grew. With technical progress, foremost the amplification used in performances by small combos since the late 1940s, its possibilities of expression and of standing its ground against louder instruments took a giant step forward. Solo playing techniques and virtuosity could be demonstrated with greater independence from the rest of the band by individually raising the volume. Blues musicians effectively used their new creative space.

A host of literature has been published on the history of the harmonica, the history of the Blues, famous players and the development of various forms of Blues-based popular music since the 1950s. There are also many instruction books on how to play the harmonica, as well as online schools. The scholarly literature I found most informative on these themes is listed in the bibliography. This work would never have been possible without it. The originality I claim lies solely in combining the threads, emphasizing the concrete relationship between the harmonica and the Blues, and putting it in a socio-political context.

During my research I have found no indication that the question of exactly how, when and where the German harmonica and the Blues musician met in the outgoing nineteenth century was ever asked. Apart from scant anecdotal evidence, we also know little about the relationship between instrument and player from the 1870s, when the harmonica began to enter the United States in tens of thousands, later in hundreds of thousands, then in millions annually, until the 1920s. Respective information is missing for the Blues and for all other musical genres in which the harmonica was used. So this cannot be explained by segregation, rather by the above-mentioned low reputation of the instrument. As to the Blues, an additional factor might come into play: It was not written music until W. C. Handy started notating it for orchestra and—paradoxically—in doing so he automatically became aloof from the "simple" intuitive players of the Blues who had no musical training. Handy did not recognize the ideal qualities of the harmonica for the Blues and never composed or arranged for it.

As the people able to shed light on what I call the "black hole" have passed on, we must look for other ways of gathering information. Maybe this little book motivates others to dig deeper. One possibility could be an intensive search of the Hohner archives bought in 1986 by the state government of Baden-Württemberg. The correspondence between the Hohner representative in New York and the factory in Trossingen since the late nineteenth century, order books and concrete deliveries in connection with the distribution system in the United States might be revelatory. If mail order companies like Sears & Roebuck or Montgomery Ward have kept archives, they might contain information where harmonicas were sold, to whom, in what frequency and volume, which keys were preferred etc. Detailed reports on the actual attendance of dealers or German manufacturers themselves at the World Fairs in the United States since the first official World's Fair in Philadelphia in 1876 could be interesting. I was able to verify that some of the most important German harmonica makers are listed in the catalogue of the Chicago Columbian Exposition of 1893, but had no time to pursue the question further.

My findings are incorporated in a freely invented story and not presented as dry non-fiction, hoping that thereby more readers will be attracted to what I find is a most fascinating relationship between a German industrial mass product and African-American musicians. The characters are completely fictional unless their full names are also mentioned in the acknowledgements. Yet, neither historical nor technical accuracy has been compromised in the process.

Acknowledgements

I have to thank foremost my wife Corinna for putting up with my being incommunicado while researching, reading and writing extensively for almost a year from mid-2014. I am deeply indebted to the current management of the two remaining German harmonica manufacturers, Christian Dehn of Hohner, and Lars Seifert of Seydel, for the opportunities they gave me to visit their factories in Trossingen and Klingenthal. In both cases a strong relationship exists with museums of the area and with historians who work full time or part time on issues related with the harmonica or the instrument industry of the region as a whole. I think of Martin Häffner, director of the German Harmonica Museum in Trossingen, and Enrico Weller, history teacher at Gymnasium Markneukirchen, with whom I conversed and whose publications I studied.

Great friends from the harmonica players' scene in the Chicago area have given me inspiration and advice, foremost the genius on the diatonic harp, Howard Levy, and the wizard, not only of customizing, Joe Filisko. For scientific consultation Greg Johnson, the librarian of the Blues Archives at University of Mississippi, always had an open ear. I had brief email exchanges with Adam Gussow and Pat Missin. Lincoln T. Beauchamp (Chicago Beau), musician and "curator of the Blues" as he calls himself, became an exceptional resource in the editing phase. He generously granted his time and contributed with invaluable advice and insights to the content. Peter Madcat Ruth made favorable comments on my draft manuscript and encouraged me to go on. Billy and Rosa Branch showed interest and shared anecdotes. Dr. Richard Erich Schade, Professor emeritus, former German Honorary Consul in Cincinnati and folk harmonica player himself, provided extremely useful editing advice and general intellectual encouragement in the final stages of the creative process. So did historian Don Heinrich Tolzmann. I thank Jesse Robinson for letting me jam with his band in *Underground 119*, Jackson, MS; Billy Branch for letting me jam at *Kingston Mines*; Smilin' Bobby at *Phyllis'*, Sugar Blue at *Rosa's Lounge*.

Dr. Connie Restle, director of the *Musikinstrumenten-Museum* in Berlin, encouraged me to follow-up on my idea of an exhibition on the German harmonica and the American Blues. The following museums, in addition to the above and *Deutsches Harmonikamuseum* in Trossingen were visited, and provided helpful insights: *Musikinstrumente Museum* in Markneukirchen, *Harmonikamuseum* in Zwota, Delta Blues Museum in Clarksdale,

MS; B. B. King Museum in Indianola, MS; National Blues Museum in St. Louis, MO; Willie Dixon's Blues Foundation, Chicago; and the Blues Foundation in Memphis, TN.

Harland Crain from Chesterfield, MO, gave me the opportunity to study his amazing private harmonica collection. I am very grateful to Tim Samuelson, city historian of Chicago, for taking me on a tour of the Blues relevant sites of the city. Peyton Prospere, Honorary Consul of Germany in Jackson, MS, provided useful hints for following the Blues trail. Bob Koester from Delmark granted me time for a talk in his Jazz Record Mart. Howard Reich, the Jazz critic of the Chicago Tribune, shared his views on Blues and Jazz with me.

Roger Stolle talked with me about his book. Theo Dasbach informed me about his autographed harmonicas. I have appreciated constructive editing advice from many friends, among them Christine Due, Judith Levi, Diane Sanofsky and others who did not want to be named.

Herbert Quelle

Chapter 1
Solicitation

"Hello, my friend. I am Monika Marine. Come play with me.

"My slightly curved, shiny metal coat hides a rectangular wooden comb body with nine teeth, square as struts. The teeth become gradually shorter from one side to the other. The space between them is far too wide for normal hair and too narrow for dreadlocks. But as I hardly leave the house without decent cover, you would not get the idea of using me for your hairdo, anyhow.

"Of my two layers of dress, my two-piece metal sheet undies are essential for my sensuality. At Monika's Secrets, where I do my shopping, you find them in the reed plates section. They have ten narrow window-like slots, perfectly matching the width of the space between the teeth and their different lengths. When I put them on the front and back of my body and look in the mirror, I get very excited and have to control immediate staircase-to-lust fantasies. I admire the ten rectangular holes between the tooth tips at the narrow top.

"I imagine your tongue touching me there. When I start affixing the twenty brass reeds, on the front near the top and on the back at the bottom, they have to fit precisely over the slots, but must be able to swing freely in it. Only the best tailors achieve both.

"I know, you would already want to press your lips on my beautifully gaping narrow top. When you blow me, the front reeds vibrate. When you suck me, you stimulate the back reeds. I love those vibrations and answer with different sounds. I can shriek and moan or give you a normal tone, loud or low, depending on your intensity. But, wait just a second. Unlike the other ladies you fool around with normally, I must be dressed to be best. So, let's go crazy by turning the screws in the nuts to affix my coat. It is necessary for you to hold, move and turn me comfortably without touching those sensitive reeds of mine. Only manipulate them with your breath.

"As we get to know each other better you will learn about my family. I am from the Richter or Haidaer lineage, a true Bohemian, so to speak. The first Marine was born in 1896. There are three other important lineages that have survived: the tremolo or Viennese, the concert and the chromatic families, but let's ignore them for now. Our impressive genealogy is clearly European, with some thousand year old Asian roots.

"And, as our creators were very (re-)productive and my forefathers liked to travel, today, my species can be found all over the world. We have existed in a range of shapes and sizes—banana, boomerang or rectangular.

"Today, our creators know that musical seriousness is best served by plain beautiful functionality. Most of our bodies are wooden or plastic and the reeds are made of brass, steel or phosphor bronze. The majority of my relatives are the size of a hand with the exception of the Chrom and Tremolo clans. Heavier, wider and longer has always been their motto.

"When my ancestors first met you, the common term applied to your ethnicity was 'Negro', although some twisted this into the derogatory term 'Nigger' as a way of defaming you and putting you down. Decades later you self identified yourself as 'Black' and today 'African-American' is the politically correct denominator. I have never minded, the Marine family was always impartial to race, no matter what my creators may have believed. Since the early days when you started exploring my entire musical eroticism and tickled all my senses, I knew we were made for each other. You owned the Blues and I could help you articulate it.

"My lover, salivate your lips and take me to new heights."

An hour after Robie called me announcing this amazing email from an unknown account, I held a print out in my hands. "Walter," he said, "there seems to be an alter ego of yours pursuing the same interest. Maybe you have to double your efforts to get your thoughts on paper."

Robie was seventy-five and my best buddy. We had known each other since the mid '60s. He owned an amazing record collection of Blues and Jazz and appropriately still lived in the South Loop, not far from 2120 South Michigan Avenue, where the Chess recording studio had been located from 1957 to 1967. He often talked about the fantastic visit of the Rolling Stones in 1964, when they recorded the instrumental with the address as the song title. The music and the anecdotes had inspired me. Not that I found Brian Jones's harp playing on that record spectacular or ever believed Keith Richards' story of Muddy Waters standing on a ladder and painting the wall as they arrived. No, there were other reasons why, for many years, I had been running around with the idea of writing about the connection between the German harmonica and the American Blues. Robie's message was a wake-up call to finally make a serious effort.

Anonymous, yes, but the sender of the email was certainly not ignorant. The lines revealed great knowledge about the instrument and the music made with it. Why had I never had the idea of deleting the first syllable "Har," spelling the name "Monika" to stress its German roots, and giving it female attributes? I also loved the alliterated surname Marine, based on the renowned

Marine Band model that the German company *Hohner* started to produce at the end of the nineteenth century for the U.S. market. And I found amazingly original, how the importance of embouchure and tongue for mastering the instrument was communicated. Admittedly, this may have to do with my masculinity. But, as most harpers were male and we currently enjoy the *50 Shades of Grey* valentine, why should harp manufacturers hide the hidden sex appeal of the instrument?

It was past midnight when I made up my mind and emailed matter of factly, "Robie, I am off to the Mississippi Delta tomorrow. Can't be reached by phone or email for a couple of days."

Before hitting the sack that night I printed a note in large letters and fixed it on my apartment door: "Temporarily Out on the Chitlin' Circuit."

Chapter 2
Setting out to search the Blues

Why did I think of the hero in the German movie by Michael Schorr *Schultze gets the Blues* from 2003, when I left my house early the next morning in my '74 beetle after a bad and agitated night? Neither had I been made redundant in a small mining town in East Germany, nor did I play accordion like Schultze. I had been living in the States for fifty years and was past retirement age. I was also not headed for a German folk music festival in New Braunfels, Texas, to play polka. But, I identified strongly with Schultze's quest for discovering something new and realizing a dream. Finally, the accordion was just a slightly more complicated instrument based on the same reeds-activated-by-air principle as the harmonica. Who knows, my old beetle and I might just meet our Lord in the American South. For the car it would be the scrapyard—although I had no doubt that it would take me there and back without a problem. For me it would be a graveyard––hopefully after experiencing something similar to Schultze's bliss in the arms of his bayou lady. Memphis was a good 500 miles or roughly eight hours drive south.

If I were still young, I would do it in a day. But I decided to rather stop near Cairo, the most southern tip of Illinois between Kentucky and Missouri at the confluence of the Ohio and Mississippi rivers.

Why there? Why not? Just six hours instead of eight, and I had never been in the Egyptian Cairo. So, should I not for once appreciate the unique offerings of the United States to visit so many interesting places of the globe (at least by name) without leaving the country, having to speak a foreign language, and being afraid of unknown germs in food or on the door knobs you need to turn to enter a new world? I remembered the great slow dance, the *Road to Cairo*, a hit by David Ackles from 1968 that I had known in the Julie Driscoll version. And what about Henry Townsend's *Cairo Blues* ". . . Women in Cairo, they will treat you kind and sweet . . ." Although that type of tickle was no longer much on my mind, I felt some weird vibrations, as if the eventual implementation of the harmonica project had finally set in motion hidden reeds in my body.

I was thinking too far ahead! The motor was not even warm yet. On my cassette, James Cotton had just paraphrased the *Jingle Bells* theme in his second solo on *Midnight Creeper*, and I was only passing the corner of Grant Park on Michigan Avenue.

Here, Central Station, the final stop of the Illinois Central rail, had received African-Americans from the

South during the first migration wave of the twentieth century between 1910 and 1930. While I was waiting at the traffic light, I looked over to the left, wondering if the Blues trail marker about the site's history was still there. With all buildings gone, the area was now covered with 106 headless– and armless bronze sculptures by the Polish artist, Magdalena Abakamovicz. I knew that to my right on Wabash I could get some provisions at the former bus depot, where from the 1930s to the 1950s the second migration wave from the Delta had arrived. Buses replacing trains, as sign of the success and the growing influence of the American motor industry. Shopping there, I showed my loyalty to Germany, as the place is now a *Trader Joe's*, the U.S. upscale version of *Aldi*. After filling my shopping basket with cookies, candy and water, I could not resist carefully opening one of the swinging doors to find a storage room with the old flooring. Goodness, did that electrify the manager behind her counter! I excused myself with having been briefly disoriented, and proceeded to the cashier. The rounded wall in one corner still attests to the previous function of the building, permitting buses easier turns when they exited the compound. My yellow Beetle did not have that problem.

Back on Michigan I drove by the former Chess studio, which is now the home of Willie Dixon's Blues Heaven Foundation. I had viewed its collection of memorabilia on various occasions, sometimes alone, sometimes with my friend Jim. Our most hilarious common visit ten years ago ran by my inner eye like a time-lapse video. Jim and I were sitting in the upstairs studio. On his lap he had this worn bone-shaped cassette-player, held together by tape, and I was sitting in front of the window to the engineering room. Both of us were moving our heads too hectically for gentlemen in their sixties to the opening riff of Chuck Berry's *Johnny B. Goode* recorded there. I recalled that, for several months after the record was released, I had thought the title was an exclamation towards Johnny to be good—such misunderstanding obviously intended by Chuck. While we were performing our head banger without hair, a group of Japanese tourists entered the room. To their great dismay we declined being videotaped and thereby certainly missed a fantastic opportunity of becoming viral stuff on YouTube.

Apart from acoustic bass player and producer Willie Dixon himself, many great artists had recorded at Chess, foremost Muddy Waters, but among them my harmonica heroes Little Walter, Howlin' Wolf and Alex (Aleck) Rice Miller, better known as Sonny Boy Williamson II.

The label's founders were two Jewish immigrants from Poland, Leonard and Phil Chess, who entered the recording business so to speak through the delivery entrance. They had owned liquor stores, then nightclubs where Black musicians performed, and finally provided these performers with recording opportunities, for which there was obviously still a demand in the Chicago of the late 1940s. In doing so, they followed in the steps of *race record* producers who in the 1920s had begun marketing to African-Americans. Despite being financially exploited, Muddy Waters and other musicians were glad that Chess got their names and music out into the world. There can be no denial that Chess helped preserve the unique heritage of the Blues women and men from the Mississippi Delta. By making records, Chess became literally a historic record keeper.

Another European immigrant who contributed to preserving the Blues was the German-American, Otto K. E. Heinemann. In 1916 he founded the race record label *Okeh* in New York, which was bought by *Columbia* in 1926. Mostly due to anti-German sentiment during and immediately after World War I, Heinemann reorganized the relationship with the German parent *Odeon* records that he represented, and renamed the American company *General Phonograph Corporation*. Okeh acknowledged the importance of the Chicago and regional Jazz and Blues scene by establishing a recording studio in the city as early as 1922. At about the same time it was probably the first to start excursions to locations in the South and elsewhere for commercial recordings. Okeh, Chess and many others were successful in catering to African-Americans, but only for a while.

How segregation in American society had affected the musical world on the performers' and on the listeners' side, had already for a while aroused my curiosity. With the development of the recording industry, the barriers between the races could theoretically be torn down, but clearly they were not. Blacks as consumers, as buyers of race records had to be specifically targeted. The owners of the means of production determined that they needed different products and outlets along racial lines. The Blues only sold to the Blues community. Smaller companies could venture easier into this market. At a time when discrimination on the basis of race was common, they did not put an established and respected "White" brand name at risk.

But when the small companies proved successful, the major corporations realized the competition and found ways to get their business.

Meditating about the recording industry and the Blues, I had missed the fastest access to the Freeway. Luckily it was only nine o'clock, so I decided to stay on Michigan and allow myself a brief stop at Oak Woods Cemetery where the harper Junior Wells had found his last rest. I had been out of the country when he passed away in 1998, but had gone to his gravesite later and personally repeated the *Taps* harp ceremony celebrated at his funeral. In doing so I honored the musician, less so the human being who clearly had many weaknesses, includ-

ing a violent way with women, as I had read in Buddy
Guy's memoir *When I Left Home*. Not far from Junior's
tomb lie the remains of Jesse Owens, the four times gold
medalist at the infamous Berlin Olympiad in 1936.
"Infamous" for Adolf Hitler's rather successful attempt to
mislead the world about the true intentions of his regime
and to test the potential of the totalitarian propaganda of
the Third Reich beyond its territorial borders. Jesse, at
least, had truly socked it to Adolf and I lifted my imagi-
nary hat, being well aware that not everything had been
gold for him in the United States either, even after his victory.

It was only while cruising slowly through this oa-
sis of peace that I realized how noisy my muffler was. The
car had not been checked properly after the long winter,
and street parking was not the best idea under the climatic
conditions of Chicago. "No problem, as long as a little
rust hole is the only thing that needs to be taken care of
after my return," I thought. At the cemetery office I asked
for directions to the interstate, because I wasn't sure any-
more and—this was really stupid—I had left my old Rand
McNally map at home. The secretary didn't know and had
to call the gardener. "Sure thin', sir," he said, "make a left
out o'the gate. Road 67 becomes Marquette," (there was
no phonetically correct resemblance to French whatsoever, could mean any market place) "turn left on Lafa-
yette," (another phonetic distortion, this time sounding
like an Italian pasta dish) "an' you gonna see signs for I-

94 East." I thanked with all my heart and without exposing my normal German habit of trying to correct the pronunciation of the French Jesuit priest who claimed the Mississippi valley and his compatriot, the Marquis, who fought a good century later in the American Revolutionary War. After all, I wanted to be back on the road, not back in the classroom.

All was well, because I followed the instructions precisely, and it was 11 a.m. as interstate 57 took me by Kankakee. About five hours net driving time left for the day. There would be a light lunch along the way—I had never been a coffee drinker and had no intention to change—and some bed in Egypt at the end, with lots of good music in between. After a bottle of water and a bag of cookies, I was feeling my bladder. "Never wait too long!" I remembered my mother saying. "Yes," I said, looking skywards and exited for the next rest area. It offered a view of plain agricultural land, prairie, rows of trees in the distance, with scattered houses in between. I took a leak in the decently maintained cubicle. Leaving the restroom, it was again the sight of the flat land that impressed me most. Plains, plains . . . But what did this guy want? I didn't see another car around. Kankakee had a prison. He kept walking towards me.

He had a Black face and Black hands and held a white sign with capital black letters that read:

"CAIRO."

Chapter 3
On the road to Cairo, Illinois

"Man, I had no excuse
caus' I looked for the Blues
so Black was good news
just what I could use
and he wore shiny shoes

So I weighed don'ts and dos
I'd avoid any ruse
and buy us some booze
and then when he'd snooze
I'd escape without boos—"

I was flabbergasted. Improvising this rap while he approached me in an elegantly swinging walk with his tender arms raising the sign with every step he had me speechless. I took a few steps back to my car.

"Pardon me, sir,
this is a little way off
the historical track
traveled by Marquette,"

(correct French pronunciation!)
"and I just want to charm
and do not mean harm."

(Falling in the previous rhythm again.)

"Okay, okay," I interrupted him, somehow sensing I was not threatened, "you must understand, just outside of Kankakee and for somebody living in the better parts of Chicago and constantly hearing these stories about Chicago's South and West Sides, and you coming out of nowhere—"

"I understand, but I'm not from nowhere,
I live in the Gold Coast
was traveling with my co-host—
Sorry—"

(He realized that his rap mania might be getting obnoxious and jeopardize his objective of hitching a ride.)

"I mean 'wife'—when we had this terrible argument. As it was her car we were driving in, she had the upper hand. She kicked me out ten minutes ago and only gave me this cardboard and a pen. My cellphone is in my jacket in the car—" (I noticed he wore only a vest over his white shirt.) "so is my wallet. I have nothing else on me."

"Where is she going?"

"Cairo." (sounding like Care-O) "She has done this before. Everything will be fine tonight. I just have to prove that I can still move—on my own. We are going to a funeral tomorrow."

Weird as it sounded, it made perfect sense to me. "Step aboard!" I invited him theatrically.

Should I apologize and reassure him that I was not prejudiced? Bullshit. Then the lines of his rap came back to me. Was he a clairvoyant mimicking my research interest?

"I'm curious. Why did you sing 'because I looked for the Blues' just now?"

"Never mind, just a rhyme.
Even if you wouldn't today,
sometime we will all want to play—
I mean discover the power
of consolation the Blues does offer."

"But you seem to be more a rapper than a Bluesman."

"I said that ironically. Yes, it's a very different attitude. Rap is a form of emancipation from the Blues music stigma."

This was going to be some interesting afternoon. I would come back to that remark later.

"Do you mind if I put on some music?"

"Not at all."

It was Little Walter's signature tune *Juke* from 1952. I explained: "You know, this is considered to be the first and prime example of direct microphone amplification used with great effect in playing the harmonica. It opened a new sound spectrum. Snooky Prior, another excellent harper, swore, however, he was the first to cup the harp and to amplify."

"I'm Luther, by the way."

"Walter—not related to the harper."

We shook hands and I turned the car key.

"Where are you headed?"

"Cairo." I replied using the CNN pronunciation for the Egyptian capital.

He looked incredulous. "What do you want there?"

"Spend the night. Then move on tomorrow."

"So, you also have friends or family down there?"

"No, I'll find a hotel."

His eyes had gotten wider, his look more bewildered by every word I said. "What?" he blurred out. "There is nothing in Cairo, nothing. The place is deserted. The last time I was there was three years ago, and I had a hard time to buy even a cup of coffee. Population is down to just over 2,000. Almost three quarters of them are my brothers and sisters. My uncle passed away, and as this was the last living family member in Cairo, this will be my last visit. Ever! And you go there voluntarily. I don't understand. You're crazy, man."

He might have a point there. I began to realize that there was a certain foolishness in my foregoing all modern technological research possibilities, and terribly naive to assume that one could find a room just like that anywhere. Especially when one was no longer young, had a high noise-sensitivity, needed a good mattress and adhered normally to more than hygienic minimum standards when going out to eat, drink and rest.

"Listen," Luther resumed his thread of thoughts, "we should arrive before sunset, and my uncle had this pretty big place with a few extra rooms and beds. So, depending on the people gathering for tomorrow, we might be able to offer you accommodation. If not, we can check on my phone, once Beth has given it back to me, what options you have along your way. There must be places around Charleston, Missouri, for example."

"Thank you. Much appreciated."

Then, Luther gave me a first insight into his life. At seven he had experienced the race riots. It was 1967, when in several American cities tensions ran so high that the National Guard had to be deployed. Cairo was just one example. He did not deny that criminal elements within the African-American community had exploited the situation. But those attempts by reactionary White politicians at the state and local level to block implementation of the Civil Rights legislation, had increased frustration to a point where centuries old anger over constant discrimination spilled over, and was released violently. Of course, as a boy under ten, he could not analyze it this way. He simply suffered and endured sleepless nights of shooting and looting in his immediate neighborhood, saw the ruins of houses still smoldering after they had been burned the previous night and missed classes, because school was closed.

Luther mentioned the lynchings of the Black man, William James, and the White man, Henry Salzner, on November 11, 1909, which had drawn a crowd five times larger than the current population to Cairo. He added cynically that perhaps one should think in this direction to revitalize the municipality. Of course, one would have to disguise the intention. One could woo investors with "one guaranteed major spectacle per year." If this was not sufficient to lure the crowds one could add something like "of Jihadi or IS proportions." I noticed how agitated he was getting. He said that the brief visit to Cairo in 1842 had inspired Charles Dickens to invent the malaria ridden swamp town Eden in his novel *Martin Chuzzlewhit*. "At least then there must have been beds for travelers," I thought.

"It's past noon. We have to get gas. Let's exit at the next rest area." I suggested. A Marathon truck stop was coming up. The dimensions of the adventure tour I had embarked on became clearer with every mile I put between my house and the unknown destination.

I found the Greek name most appropriate. I had a lot of respect for people who, in two hours and a few minutes, ran distances that I had never even walked in a whole day. My Greek-American friend Demos, who owned the little restaurant *Europa and the Bull* in my block would have been proud of my choice. Being an expert in Greek history and mythology he would be fully aware of the challenge I faced. His authority was only damaged—and there were many occasions—when he explained the debt crisis with the Gods. I never argued with him. Otherwise he might deny me the complimentary shot of ouzo that was an added attraction to the good food served at his place.

In the coffee shop we took seats at the counter. Luther felt uncomfortable, as he did not have money on him. I reassured him it was not a problem. If it felt better for him, he could pay me later. Both of us had a burger with fries and cola. "How predictable," one might think, but for me this was rather unusual. I liked pasta and prepared it in all variations. Yet, being mostly not cooked "al dente" in American eateries, pasta was never as safe a bet as beef patties. He finished with a cup of coffee. I settled the check and went to the restroom.

When restarting the engine, the noise from the exhaust was awfully loud. The various rhythm and blues pieces we had heard on the way, and my concentration on Luther's Cairo tales and so forth had apparently masked the sound. I drove over to the pump and filled the tank. Luther had offered to do that, but I was afraid they might ask him to stay on as an attendant.

Leaving the gas station with our roaring rear, we turned the windows down. I had to decide about the urgency of a repair. Before I could say how much the noise embarrassed me, I noticed the flashing blue light in my rearview mirror and heard the siren every driver fears. We were still on the grounds of the truck stop and I pulled over immediately. It made me mad that they interrupted Howlin' Wolf's *Highway 49*. The police could have stopped short of their second howl. But it took half the song until they cut it out. "Hopefully only decibel sadists!" I muttered. Luther had sunk into his seat and checked the safety belt, an expression of unease on his face, then a sudden nervousness, sweat pearls on his brow, a loud "Shi-it" from his mouth. His hands touching intensely over and over all pockets of his pants, slapping his thighs, raising his butt.

"Ho-ho-hold it right there!" came from the right side of the car. The cop's gun was just behind Luther's head and my situation was not much better with a second cop on my side.

Somewhat friendlier he asked me "Everything all right, sir? I'd like to see your driver's license and insurance papers." They must have had a lunch break reunion, because a second car pulled up beside the one whose team had stopped us. I suddenly realized why my companion had become so excited. If his wife had taken his jacket with his wallet and cellphone, he probably would not have any ID on him. I guessed what that meant.

"May I ask why you are stopping me, officer?" I foolishly queried. "I know that calling my muffler a muffler is an insult to every real muffler," I was quick to correct my mistake and try to be funny at the same time, "but I am going to find a repair shop." I made that up while talking. "Can I reach in my left jacket pocket for my license? The insurance proof is in the glove compartment."

"Wait!" he replied and nodded to the officer on the other side who had during these seconds watched closely that Luther kept sitting on his hands.

"What the fuck do I do?" ("I wished I knew, don't you see I am new—" my companion might have added under less stressful circumstances.)

"Keep your gun pointed. Grab his neck and push his head to the dashboard. Then ask him to slowly pull his right hand from under his butt and put it on the dashboard with the palm up, then the same for the left hand."

Luther was in obvious mental pain, but maintained his calm and cooperated, thank God. As I saw Luther in that position I thought of a praying Muslim. In order to be perfect, he would have to be not only literally but physically on his knees.

"And now?" the other asked his mentor next to me.

"Open the door, and he gets out turning his lower body towards you, leaving the hands where they are as long as possible. Then you take three steps back still pointing, of course, and he can use his hands for grabbing the top frame of the door to get out. Then he should turn towards the car, spread-eagle, with his hands firmly touching the roof."

Hoping that this nightmarish situation would soon have a happy ending, I watched as Luther complied with the instructions the cop on my side gave to his colleague.

Silently I congratulated him for managing this without visible commotion. He surely had seen the procedure in many films. Obviously, he also belonged to the lucky ones whose parents had drilled their kids not to resist and to remain polite, especially when encountering White policemen. "But I say unto you, resist not him that is evil but whosoever smiteth thee on thy right cheek, turn to him the other also." Was it Mathew 5:39?

The left hand of the cop was fondling Luther up-wards across the chest where his hand stopped. "What do we have here?"

"I don't know, officer, sir!" Luther replied.

The cop reached under the vest and pulled some-thing out of the shirt pocket. "Luther Vanguard," he shouted loud enough so that the cop in the second car could copy,

"Goethe Street," (The way he said the street name was torture to my ears!) "Chicago, IL 60610. Let's run a check on that. I couldn't afford living at that zip code. That much I know."

Did I notice correctly that in the very same mo-ment the cop pulled his hand from Luther's breast, the ten-sion and stiffness of my companion's body, which could be sensed without seeing him fully from my angle, had given way to an almost orgiastic relaxation? Apparently it was his picture ID. Later he would tell me that he had tak-en it out of his wallet the day before, because he needed to make a photocopy, and then not put it back. By sheer luck he saw it on his desk near the copier this morning, and as he had already hung the jacket in the car, put it subcon-sciously in his shirt pocket.

Luther's cop had in the meantime also checked the

car seat for any concealed weapon, found the insurance proof in the glove compartment, exchanged looks with the cop behind us, and finally signaled all clear. Under careful eyes I finally pulled out my wallet and handed the driver's licence to my cop. Even if the papers were in good order, I suspected there might still be something else. The second police car drove off, but I wasn't yet sure this had been it.

"We observed you at the counter and at the pump with him staying in the car." he said. "Why did you pay his check? Is there something going on between the two of you that we should know, sir? You're safe now. But we can't do much for you, once you are on the road again."

"Thank you, officer, but don't worry." I was sure he would not be satisfied without an explanation, which fit perfectly the parameters of his narrow-mindedness, and did not raise any new suspicions. So, something like "We are brothers in soul and love the Blues and perchance met, because his wife kicked him out and we have to be in Cairo tonight." was definitely not permitted and unforgivable. Despite living in a better area of Chicago than his White companion, Luther should appear to have an inferior place in society. Otherwise these guys might not be too happy. On the other hand, he must have a solid employment, so that they were convinced Luther had no reason to follow any low instincts of a criminal nature.

"Luther is a butler. He lives in the same house as

my frail brother, Brad, who had a more successful career than I, and is the retired CEO of a major corporation. As Brad is very fond of Luther, he asked his chauffeur to drive him to Cairo for his uncle's funeral tomorrow morning. An emergency nurse was organized, because Brad needs 24/7 care. Then, this morning the chauffeur called in sick. But, you see, Luther very rarely drives and was reluctant to take either the Rolls Royce or the Ferrari himself. So my brother called me to drive Luther, which I am glad to do, as I had no plans anyhow, officer. I insisted, however, to take my own car, because I am also not familiar with these luxury models. And, you know better than I do that public transport to and from Cairo is impossible. Luther can only be back tomorrow evening by being chauffeured."

Both policemen had listened with great interest and I saw that I hit the right spot. They nodded so approvingly that I was afraid they might get whiplash. Then I dared to risk a question. "Would it be possible at all, officer, that the necessary repair of my exhaust could be postponed till after my return to Chicago?" It certainly helped that Luther had slumped into the posture of utter servitude to create a favorable atmosphere for examining this request.

"You shouldn't believe those media lies. We are not inhuman." they said simultaneously, shoving their guns back into their holsters. Then, the more experienced indicated his consent, looking at his partner. "We haven't heard that much noise, really. Have a safe trip!" They focused on me exclusively. Luther had become nonexistent. When we drove off, they briefly held their hands over their ears.

We were back on track. After Howlin' Wolf there was a compilation of Buddy Guy and Junior Wells songs which gave us a pleasant enough excuse to remain silent for some miles.

Distance and time we both needed to come to terms with what had just happened. It was Luther who spoke first.

"Quite a story you dished out to them. Very skillful! I'm not offended at all. Butler is a respectable profession. I have to admit, it's very unusual for a person with a deep suntan to live in my building. The elevator's dark woodwork is otherwise only lit by pale English. If the cops had known that I make really good money with the production of TV-commercials, they might have jumped to unpleasant conclusions. Doesn't that involve fancy studio work with glamorous girls and lots of partying? Surely the guy digs dope! You played it really safe, man, and to my great surprise, got me out of there without a scar. They were tame as lambs in the end. And getting away with this broken muffler is truly amazing. No, really, I already saw them give us the full program. What would you have said, if they asked for permission to search the car for drugs? Do you know that you can refuse? (I did not.) Of course, for me who has the same rights as you but darker skin, saying 'No' would nevertheless not have been advisable. If I had been alone just now, I probably would have accepted the additional harassment rather than give them incentives for further steps. Man, it's a tough world, we live in, you wouldn't believe it." (I knew that he was not speaking of foreign countries.) "Thank you. Thank you. Thank you."

I showed no immediate reaction. I hoped that sympathetic silence was enough consolation.

Should I linger on the subject? Or should I distract him. In half an hour we must cross Highway 16 connecting Gays with Paris. Ah, *joie de vivre.* Some twenty odd miles on there lay Effingham, the most beautiful taboo deformation city name for the most used four letter word. It was no good to respond to the seriousness of the points he had raised with puerile comments, I decided.

"You know, Luther, *you* may not believe this, but I take the point you make very seriously. I see myself in the tradition of singer-songwriters of the '60s and '70s and compose songs and write socially critical lyrics and just the other day—"

"You do what?" he interrupted me.

"I occasionally perform my stuff, and just the other day I finished the lyrics of a new song which deals with racial discrimination in the States. Of course, my German background shines through. If you want to hear it, I will recite it. If you prefer to read it, there's a copy in the side pocket of my carry-on bag on the backseat."

"Why don't you sing it? I'm really surprised. You––don't take me wrong—don't look like a singer-songwriter."

"What the—look, Effingham coming up—" I giggled pointing to the road sign, "does that mean, 'don't look like'? Do you think you know how a singer-songwriter looks? Take Pete Seeger, Woody Guthrie, Bob Dylan, Joan Baez and hundreds others? Don't they have at least in common that they all look different in their normalcy? Other than pop grandees who have to match certain fashion ideals." I felt that my voice had gotten slightly agitated and ended in a sotto voce "Sorry."

"Come on, I'm curious."

"I can't sing it now. It's called 'Bad—' or maybe 'White Bad Conscience Blues'. Let me try to remember the lyrics. The first verse goes like:

"On MLK day I was reading this book
and being a White man I didn't feel good'
—I'm still undecided whether to say White man or whitie—

'On MLK day I was reading this book

29

and being a White man I didn't feel good.
So, despite wearing German and not Southern shoes
I was getting White bad conscience Blues."

The second verse:

"It's been fifty years since the voting rights laws
and seventy years since the Holocaust'
–that's where my German background shows, you see—
'It's been fifty years since the voting rights laws
and seventy years since the Holocaust
I felt pain in my German not American shoes
all this gave me the bad conscience Blues."

And the third and fourth:

"At the State of the Union the President spoke
'bout the country's achievements and
that it ain't broke
At the State of the Union the President spoke
'bout the country's achievements and
that it ain't broke
It was broadcast widely, made global news,
while ignoring the bad conscience Blues."

"In parts of this country when traveling around
there's bigotry and racism still to be found

In parts of this country when traveling
around
there's bigotry and racism still to be found
I hate to sound righteous but believe in this
truth
Without soul searching you're stuck with the
Blues."

Luther's rising emotions could be sensed while I was slowly and with occasional interruptions reciting my work in progress from memory. Every word had still to be joined with the right note and expressed in the right way. The melody idea in the key of G was ready. In addition to the basic twelve bar form, it met other standard Blues requirements like the flattened 3rd, but I wanted to alternate the flattened 7th with a major 7 to give it a slightly elaborated jazzy touch. Rhythmically it should swing. Knowing my limits as a singer, I might give Luther a taste of the melody on a *Hohner Special 20* or *Seydel 1847* I was carrying along, if he insisted.

When practicing the song, I always added licks of *America, the Beautiful* in the breaks, asking myself whether this kind of political irony would not be too offensive for White America. Whereas any attempt of mine to sing the Blues would sound like a sacrilege, I did not feel awkward playing it on the harmonica. After all, the instrument that so much enriched the range of musical expression of the African-American player, was of German origin. Using the Blues *form* was no problem either, as it belongs to mankind as a whole. One does not take anything away from its creators. On the contrary, one gives back by honoring the treasure. In order to be authentic, my lyrics had to be more sophisticated than genuine Blues lyrics, because my educational background was vastly different from that of the Blues people. If I wanted to be respected, I needed to keep a respectful distance from the original.

I don't know whether I said any of this aloud, but Luther understood immediately when I declined to sing.

"Despite the shortcomings of my voice, I will have to sing the song eventually myself, if I want it to be heard. The text is so highly personal. I wonder if there could ever be persuasive cover versions. Maybe I could generate the Blues feeling by a combination of reciting the lyrics with some harp accompaniment. The instrument allows this nice compromise, as it probably comes closest to the human voice.

"The list of awesome African-American harpers is long. They are out of reach of my playing abilities. Among them are Blues Birdhead, DeFord Bailey, Sonny Terry, the two Sonny Boy Williamsons, Little Walter Jacobs, Walter Horton, Junior Wells, James Cotton, Bill Boy Arnold, Jimmy Reed, Billy Branch, Sugar Blue and many others. If one day we begin talking about the World Musical Heritage, the Blues must be recognized as belonging to it. I cannot identify so much with Rap and Hip Hop. I find some of it too aggressive or even violent, in particular in videos where music and images resemble a porn clip."

"Wow, I am truly impressed." Luther said. "How did you become so interested in the Blues? And where are you headed after Cairo?"

Indeed, I had not yet told him about my trip. "I am on my way to the Mississippi Delta to visit the Blues trail. I want to write a book about the role of the German harmonica in Blues music. Much later than playing a little Blues harp myself as a teen did I realize that the guys I was trying to imitate, like Canned Heat or John Mayall were not the creators and representatives of Blues as a lifestyle, but just very impressive representatives of Blues as a genre. Living in Chicago and with more leisure time towards retirement, I have become more and more aware of the role the city plays for the Blues. Not that it has always been especially kind to the musicians. But, it is a fascinating place to study the topic. And reading Leroy Jones or Amiri Baraka, as he later renamed himself, I understood that the history of the Blues and the history of the African-American people are inseparable. Do you know his books *Blues People* and *Black Music*? In *Blues People* he philosophizes somewhat lengthily about how the history explains the music and vice versa. He also doubts generally that Whites or middle-class African-

Americans can sing the Blues. I didn't need Baraka to know that I can't sing the Blues. And whether you, as middle—or is it upper-class African-American can be a Blues singer, is something impossible for me to judge unless you give me a demo."

"What's the guy's name? Amir Barack? No? Got it, Amiri Baraka. As you can guess from my question, I haven't read him. Honestly, this Black consciousness stuff has never really interested me and I think, you Germans moralize too much. But I must admit, now that you put it in context, this brings us back to the attitude question—the stigma of the Blues—I mentioned earlier. Anyway, I find it amazing you are digging deeper into this than I ever have."

"I have to read about it, if I want to learn. You know it, because you are part of the community."

"I know it all right, but that doesn't mean that I understand it better than someone like you who is only reading about it. Being part of something can shut you off from seeing the truth. You cannot have a true vision of yourself and of the circumstances you are living in without breaking out of or being liberated from your mold."

"Well, just describe your feelings about the Blues and then I will give you more of my own thoughts on the music and maybe describe in more detail where I agree with Baraka and where I disagree."

"This is actually the first time I am seriously challenged about my prejudice against the Blues. I am fifty-five, in a sort of private emergency, hitching a ride with a White guy—how old are you?—okay, fifteen years my senior, to Cairo of all places, discussing the Blues.

> "Wow, isn't this weird,
> just after we cleared
> the cops who I feared
> my driver appeared
> to be smarter than shit
> on the road that we hit
> and we really did fit
> until we would split–

"Let me be quite frank—I hope, I don't offend you and your high appreciation of the Blues—"

"You won't," I assured him, "my opinion should be totally irrelevant." I saw the big question mark forming between his lower lip and his eyebrows. "Never mind. I'll explain later."

"I think early Blues is primitive, both structurally and in content; played by uneducated people who sang grammatically flawed, simple lyrics in an often barely comprehensible pronunciation. The themes were limited, mostly relating to travel or how their mama either did or didn't treat them right. You know that very often the language was sexually explicit.

"The guitar riffs were unimaginative and repetitive, the turn-arounds predictable. It became a little better after the Second World War and with wider instrumentation like by including the harmonica," (I got a sparkle in my eyes and glanced at him from the side.) "but in principle, I was always rather embarrassed to hear it and could not really enjoy it."

"You may be surprised that this verdict does not surprise me at all." I replied. "And, what I am going to say is hopefully not offensive to you, either. I am talking about something that has only affected me as an on-looker, never as a participant. I still don't know whether you can sing the Blues. But your opinion corroborates observations by Baraka and some sociologists on the typical behavior of the Black middle class in the States that distanced itself from its cultural heritage, and tried to re-invent itself with a new identity. In order to become acceptable in their new neighborhoods, to demonstrate how they had risen on the social ladder, they felt obliged to change their consumption habits, including music. Jazz was always more sophisticated than Blues, and remained an acceptable form of expression and listening habits. But the appreciation of the Blues, although being essential for the development of Jazz, faded. Its importance as genuine identifier of a people gave way to it being important as music only. And as music only it became subject to taste criteria and was exposed to the laws of the musical fashion cycle. The positive side effect was, of course that now, independently from its sociological context, the Blues could be used by other players, and appreciated by other audiences.

"It was a long way from the porch or the street corner, where Negroes hollered and strummed their guitars and were visited by White ethnologists, via the kitchen where Blacks listened to race records produced for them, or the juke where Blacks sang for a Black crowd, to a club on Chicago's North side, where the audience of Junior Wells or Muddy Waters consisted mostly of Whites. Early country Blues reflected a mood that the migrants from the Delta to the city sought to put behind them as soon as a step up the social ladder permitted.

"The urban Blues of the late '40s through '60s in whose creation Chicago was so influential, opened new possibilities, but—is that paradoxical or not?—its decline in the Black community coincided with the eventual success of the Civil Rights Movement. In parallel a Blues wave, including an increase in the use of the harmonica, broke over Europe—not only in Britain, as most Americans point out, but very significantly in Germany and France.

"The legal liberation of the African-Americans, 100 years after the Emancipation Proclamation, almost seems to have been the nail in the coffin of the Blues. There was such a euphoria about final full emancipation that cultural identity markers like the Blues seemed to stand in the way of integration into modern American society. I guess, Baraka might argue that for the most part your brothers and sisters did not realize that they still stayed in the same ghetto, only in an improved one. That's just how segregation continues to work in a very sophisticated way in today's officially desegregated society, exceptions like yours proving the rule. And, of course, drawing conclusions from what we experienced earlier at the rest area, we probably concur that there are still problems. I leave it to you to judge. I am not even competent enough to be the spokesperson of the many White underdogs in this country who have problems with the state.

"But, I believe that generally the initial contact with the law is different, dependent on race. A case involving a White person is burdened with less racial prejudice than a case involving an African-American. My opinion about the judicial system may be based more on conjecture than hard evidence, but I could give you many concrete examples of race-based prejudices in my community. So, as controversial and uncomfortable as Baraka may be, he has a certain point."

These sociological observations in reply to Luther's harsh verdict on the music were still incomplete without a nice musical piece demonstrating its best qualities.

"Luther, you mind holding on to the steering wheel?" We were doing 65 mph and there was not much traffic. While I kept my foot steady on the gas, I fumbled with the cassettes and had to take my glasses off to read several covers. The last time I had done this, was some forty years before on the German autobahn with my then girlfriend in a Mercedes 200, at ninety miles per hour. "Here it is." I took over from Luther again who looked a little anxious and put in the Okeh label recording *Mean Low Blues* from 1929 by Blues Birdhead, whose real name was James Simons.

"Who's playing the clarinet or trumpet?" Luther asked after the first two bars of this twelve bar slow Blues with its beautiful New Orleans Jazz feel. I did not respond right away, in order to give him time to realize by himself that he had been misled by one of the greatest harpers of all times. Astonishment was showing on Luther's face. He had noticed that the instrument he heard was actually a harmonica, and that the accompaniment was a very sophisticated piano, not the "unimaginative guitar" he had derided before as characteristic of prewar Blues. His astonishment climaxed when I told him this was recorded ten years before the Second World War.

"I had no idea."

"I tell you, there are treasures out there. And today it's so easy to find them on the web. It is funny to follow online discussions among harmonica aficionados

39

about *Mean Low Blues* being the first recording ever with an overblow. I can get lost on YouTube occasionally." I admitted. "But, the web can, of course, also contain some bullshit. The greatest problem is distinguishing between reliable and misleading information. Take the English Wikipedia entry on the harmonica factories in Germany for example? I recently found the entry that C.A. Seydel had manufactured the instrument in Trossingen. The Seydel site has, however, always been in Klingenthal, Saxony, which is about 300 miles northeast of Trossingen. By the way, it was founded in 1847 and is the oldest still operating harmonica producer in the world!"

"Did you say 1847? Are you sure? That's awesome!"

"Far less obvious is a false claim I discovered in the entry on the harmonica itself, repeating the common belief that it was played by President Abraham Lincoln. For my research project this was a perfect setting. The great defender of the Union, under whose presidency slavery was incidentally abolished, playing the mouth harp at about the same time that the German instrument makers started exporting on a large scale to the United States; the former slaves also getting access to the instrument, which helped them in their emancipatory struggle. Luckily, I thought, 'Too good to be true.' So I verified with the Lincoln Presidential Library in Springfield, Illinois. They would have loved to confirm, but unfortunately they couldn't. All the records showed that Abe had been totally amusical. There was no indication that he had possessed a harmonica. When I argued that one of the sympathetic things about the harmonica was that simply by doing what is essential for human survival in the first place, namely inhaling and exhaling, you could already produce two corresponding and nicely sounding chords, they shrugged it off. I remained stubborn that even if one were absolutely without any musical inclination, the harmonica was the easiest instrument to access. Yet they insisted there was forgery involved. A harmonica manufacturer like Hohner did, of course, grasp the opportunities rather than question the truth. This explains their advertisements from 1927 until today connecting Lincoln and the harp. Later I discovered that the false information is refuted also in Ken Field's great book *Harmonicas, Harps and Heavy Breathers*. In the way of compensation, Field gives us other U.S. presidential harmonicists: Woodrow Wilson, Calvin Coolidge, Dwight Eisenhower and Ronald Reagan."

Apparently, my enthusiasm about the musicality of U.S. presidents had not exactly had the calculated effect. As I looked over, Luther had dozed off. It was still seventy miles to go. I let him sleep.

Chapter 4
Cairo

Just before exit 1, I woke Luther up. He startled briefly, then gave me clear directions to his uncle's house. It was 5:10 p.m. on a Monday and a light drizzle fell. The humidity had risen. There was a pleasant surprise, as we got off the Interstate and saw a decent looking motel just across the intersection. Luther understood the motion of my head. We crossed railroad tracks, and in a wide bend turning south reached Future City. If it didn't carry that name, I might have been less depressed as we passed through, but certainly my future and that of everybody dear to me deserved something more promising. As we entered Cairo proper, we crossed the same railroad as before, only that it was now running in an easterly direction towards the bridge over the Ohio. Behind the underpath lay another old railway track, obviously no longer used. To our right a school building with an almost empty parking lot—school must be over, but I had to ask Luther's family whether it was still operating at all—a now defunct motel on the right, followed by an uninviting gas station. I was not yet running on reserve, but getting tight. We passed unoccupied houses in bad outer shape, a deserted supermarket, and a cumulation of signs that life had left the place, but nothing compared to the wasteland with burnt out ruins that I had seen before in Detroit. Compared to my prior information about Cairo this was somewhat better, proving again that there is always a big difference between read and see.

"At the end of Sycamore, the street we're on, there lies the impressive National Guard brick-building that played an important role in controlling the riots in the sixties." Luther said. "But we are not going that far. You want to turn right on 31st and then left on Washington Avenue."

Immediately after we got on Washington, I saw this sleeping beauty on my side of the street with a white painted wrought-iron gate frame that read "Riverlore." Diagonally opposite is an even more impressive three-story mansion in slightly better shape at first sight, "Magnolia Manor." Detecting precisely where I was looking, Luther said, "Both buildings are from the late nineteenth century, and on the registrar of historical places. By the way, you can pull up behind that mauve pick-up truck. Family seems to have come in great numbers." I did as he had suggested and saw a quite impressively sized single-family home with dramatic laminate peel-off, without any ornamentations, just a few houses down from Riverlore and Magnolia. There was a long line of parked cars in front of us. We got out of the beetle. As soon as Luther was standing by the car, I heard somebody shouting loudly, in high pitch and with a hysterical twist, "Darlin', I missed you sooo much. Come to Mamie. I knew you would make it."

In the somewhat overgrown garden a beautiful lady in her late forties was jumping up and down and waving towards Luther. The line from Townsend's *Cairo Blues* about Cairo women treating you sweet came back to me in a split second.

"Beth, honey, I'll be right over. You see," he addressed me in a subdued voice, "everything's gonna be all right—she's already in that stage now. And it's just a matter of the next few hours until I put up with it again, too. It's crazy, but you know, some women are regularly beaten-up by their men, and yet they still keep crawling back to them. I have never raised my hand against her, and she has kicked me out on the road eleven times. I love her. She's a great woman and my advantage seems to be the acquaintances I am forced to make. But," he hit my shoulder hard, "nobody has ever been as interesting as you, Walter. Come on, I'll introduce you to my folks."

The late afternoon sun had come out again after the light shower on our way in, and the moisture, gathered in the grounds, evaporated over the shrubs and the grass where family members of Arthur Raws, half somber, half gay and not all in dark clothes had reunited for the sad occasion of his funeral. Beth jumped up at Luther who was still half a head taller despite her high heels, closing her gorgeous legs around him, kissing his face all over while folding her hands over his ears. Luther supported her butt still passionless, like a gymnast or dancer would do, with prescribed, meticulously executed moves.

I was the only White face and everybody welcomed me naturally. The questions would be shot at Luther. But I had so many questions myself. One of them being, "How come the deceased lived in this neighborhood?" This was partly answered, when I saw Arthur who lay for the viewing in the living room with the top half of the coffin open. A gentleman in uniform, rank Lieutenant Colonel of the U.S. Army, with full decorations on his breast. He looked no longer commanding, but having willingly obeyed his last command on earth.

Nicely groomed, and very smart. I later learned that this was not only due to successful makeup efforts by the funeral company. He had kept himself in good shape till his final breath at eighty-four. Admittedly, the house had not been quite able to keep up with him, as I looked around, but it was not in a dilapidated state either. Obviously, his pension had been enough for himself, but not much money had been spent on the interior of the first floor. No signs of a companion under the same roof.

A twenty-five year old grandson named James introduced himself to me. The first thing he said was

"Grandpa loved the Blues. He brought a harmonica collection from his service in Germany. He played a little, but never advanced very much. His favorite players were Jazz Gillum and Sonny Boy Williamson II." I beamed with joy. This was my man. I bowed to the deceased. A lady elegantly dressed in a dark suit with a silvery blouse, approached me, "Can I get you some coffee or soft-drink, Mister? James, what are you telling the gentleman?"

"Thank you, Miss, I would love some lemonade. Mansion-type houses like this always awaken my thirst for homemade lemonade. I'm Walter by the way."

"Janice. So nice to meet you." She shook my hand. She was tall and well-built, in her mid-fifties, short hair. "So you've already met my son, and you seem to have something to talk about. I'll get your drink."

James and I moved into the adjoining room and sat down on a sofa. There we had a good view of the living room with Arthur's coffin, and through a second room into the dining room. The table there, which could easily accommodate eight people, was loaded with food on plastic and paper plates, large soda bottles and plastic cups. Nobody made an effort to create a more appealing presentation, and none of the thirty or so guests seemed to mind.

When somebody announced the undertakers would come in a few minutes and take the body away, there was a lot of commotion. Many wanted to have another last look at Arthur. I saw no tears. The general mood was that of gratefulness, both for a long and rich life, which they had more or less shared, and for a peaceful passing.

"Our mother has been dead for over twenty years now." Janice handed me the lemonade, prepared freshly unless the aroma deceived me. "She drowned on a beach in Louisiana. She had never learned to swim. It happened while Dad was asleep on the sand.

"It took him ten years to get over it. Maybe he lied to us and never really coped, but in the last years he no longer talked about the accident. So we assumed he was okay. That's been the one tragic incident in the family. Arthur's case is different. The way he left this world makes me really envious."

"You're too young to even think of death." I said.

"I believe one is never too young to think of death as the greatest certainty there is in life." was her reply. "Excuse me, I think the undertaker has arrived." Janice left and I asked James to introduce me to his father. "Sorry, man. Dad walked out of the house when I was twelve and never came back. He had another woman. Thank God, I'm an only child and Grandpa insisted that Mother get a good education. She could support the two of us, and was financially strong enough to get me through college. I majored in business admin this year."

"Congrats on your graduation. I am sorry about your father. Janice must be about the same age as Luther." I guessed.

"Exactly. They were both born in 1960, only two months apart. Arthur and his sister lived further down by what is today Dr. Martin Luther King Ave and 5th. Do you want to see Arthur's harp collection?"

I was surprised by the sudden change of topic, but James needed not ask twice. We walked up to the second floor while the coffin was carried to the waiting car in the driveway. When we opened the right door on the landing, it was like entering a private salon with the best of the German Harmonica Museum in Trossingen. What Arthur had saved in expenditure downstairs, he had invested in the presentation of these exhibits. There were custom made walnut cabinets with glass fronts and built-in cupboards with sliding glass doors. When James dimmed the chandelier, a beautifully balanced and warm light fell on the displayed treasures.

The harmonicas without boxes had clearly been polished not too long ago. Their dignity of age was in their patina. The glitter from the reflection of the metal covers was not so bright on those harmonicas that were half hidden in or on their boxes, because the box-lids cast discreet shadows. I sensed this was deliberately arranged to make the presentation more varied and interesting. No expense had been spared. The interior decorator must have known what he was doing. I only later learned that Arthur himself had designed all this and after retirement at fifty-eight had slowly taken up his boyhood hobby of woodwork. With the assistance of a local carpenter and helpers who were glad to have something to do in Cairo's economic downturn, Arthur had during three years built this room. I could picture the deceased sitting in the armchair near the only window, the curtains drawn, and dreaming of the times gone by when the first of these instruments were made.

"What's behind those two solid doors by the armchair?" James walked over. "They're not doors, they are drawers." He pulled them open one by one. "Grandpa didn't want to disturb the overall atmosphere of mechanical instruments for himself and for the occasional visitor. Neither did he want to forego the pleasure of listening to his beloved music, so he had this easy-to-operate sound system installed."

When James pushed a button on the first drawer, a board moved smoothly up to the height of the arms of the chair, in the middle was an elegant aluminum box, resembling stacked external hard drives. Next to it, lay a remote control with a large display, and headphones. All of this was flanked by a pair of high-end speakers. The second drawer contained a time-tested jukebox mechanism for bringing vinyl records to the front and putting them to play.

"Arthur digitized most of his harmonica Blues using the latest technology. Occasionally he would, however, yearn for analog audio. Then his old 78s from Okeh, Emerson, Vocalion, Victor or Paramount and all these 45s from post World War II labels came into play. There are a few hundred in that tunnel behind the wall. You could argue, the vinyl would match nicely with the harmonicas, but he didn't see it that way."

I wondered how the mechanics managed the difference between the record shapes and speeds. James' explanation had brought my attention back to the displays, the real treasures of the salon.

In one corner a cabinet containing harmonicas labeled *DDR*, immediately attracted my attention. All sorts of thoughts went through my head. I appreciated that Arthur used the German acronym of *Deutsche Demokratische Republik* instead of *GDR* for *German Democratic Republic*. In 1964 there were still seven harmonica producers in the German Democratic Republic. 1964 was also the year in which the late West German promoters, Horst Lippmann & Fritz Rau—both in the Blues Hall of Fame in Memphis—organized an East Germany tour for Howlin' Wolf, after he had attended the American Folk and Blues Festival in the Federal Republic of Germany. It would be interesting to know if he took a GDR harp home. 1965 saw the first and only tour of Louis Armstrong and his All Stars across the German Democratic

Republic. In 1967 Junior Wells and Big Joe Turner toured there. Back in Chicago, I would have to check if I still had their vinyl *Vietnam Blues/ Roll'em Pete*, released by the East German label *AMIGA*.

Visits of African-American Jazz and Blues stars in the German Democratic Republic were more an exception than a rule and they had to fit into the regime's propaganda. Whereas the GDR followed the general line of the socialist block that the United States represented the worst of Western imperialism and capitalism, some Black artists were welcome. By inviting them, the GDR intended to show that she was differentiating between the people and the system. And she wanted to make a political statement against discrimination. There was certainly always an attempt to instrumentalize the artists for political purposes.

James continued, "Arthur retired in Germany, just when the Wall came down in November 1989. A few days later, he traveled to the region in Western Saxony right on the Czech border—"

I interjected, "Today that area is appropriately marketed as *Musicon Valley*. During the final years of the GDR the so-called *People's Owned Company Klingenthal Harmonica Factories*—in German, *VEB Klingenthaler Harmonikawerke*—had combined resources and knowledge there, with *Seydel & Söhne* being an important part of it."

"Anyway. He went straight to the factory gate. He asked whether and where he could get all of the twenty-four different models produced that year. It took him two days to satisfactorily accomplish this goal. He proved to be a great tradesman. When the VEB tried to cheat him, by offering sales at a ratio of one West-German mark for one East-German mark, while the de facto exchange rate was more like one to ten, he outfoxed them with a complicated dollar conversion scheme and finally got them to accept something like one to twenty. So, his impressive collection of the last harmonicas produced in the GDR before the German unification began, cost him barely twenty dollars. They might be worth at least thirty times that amount today."

I stared at James, while he told me this anecdote. He was all enthusiasm and curiosity. His face dissolved into the surface of a lake, on which I projected a brief history of the German harmonica industry, hoping to produce some ripples, "Seydel is again a thriving business with top quality instruments, manufactured at its founding place in Klingenthal next to the gate where Arthur stood." I began. "The owners are Germans from outside the region. In Trossingen, Hohner, just ten years younger than Seydel, is still going strong. Although as part of a global corporation with a much wider production line and no longer controlled by German capital. The beginnings in both regions lie in the late 1820's. Both places are relatively remote, with valleys and tall mountains, harsh winters and not very fertile lands. I wondered why the harmonica had its roots there, until I realized that in the age before trains and cars, overland speed was pretty restricted, independent of the terrain."

James demonstrated what he had learned at university, "Wouldn't the difficulty of transporting heavy goods across mountains be a more important factor than speed? We are not dealing with perishable goods."

"You're right. I just wanted to say that remoteness, slow speed and self-centered attitudes may have combined to produce a certain ingenuity in the people living in those parts. Johann Wilhelm Glier of Klingenthal started German harmonica manufacturing in 1829 according to reliable accounts. Langhammer from Bohemia, just across the border from Saxony, might have been producing as early as 1823. Christian Messner, Trossingen, took up harmonica production in 1827, and Friedrich Hotz from Knittlingen in Württemberg came next in the 1830s. Your uncle's collection contains some of their instruments. Are you interested in not only preserving but expanding his collection? The way you talk shows me that you recognize their value.

"In Hohner's first decade, from 1857 to 1867, almost all of its production was exported to the United States. Towards the end of the nineteenth century, the

Austrian share of about one hundred harmonica manufacturers in Germany and Austria diminished.

"By 1900, harmonica production is practically an all-German affair. When the boom comes to an end around 1930, at the height of the depression, which also halts the first major immigration wave of African-Americans from the Mississippi Delta to Chicago, the few remaining German manufacturers were the only ones left.

"By 1930 Hohner had triumphed over most of its German competitors and clearly dominated the global market, with particular success in the United States. According to its own account, Hohner surpassed by 1986— yes, Arthur was already stationed in Germany—an accumulated production of one billion harmonicas since its foundation. More than 700 million Hohners were exported to the United States.

"For me there is this metaphysical link between a German industrial product and the African-American soul. For you these thoughts will probably be new, but I have frequently imagined the working conditions of the Black slaves and later sharecroppers in the cotton fields during the second half of the nineteenth century, and compared them with the conditions of the German cottage workers who were indispensable in harmonica manufacturing until industrialization kicked in on a grand scale. Poverty was a common trait. But social, political and legal restrictions were much lower on the German side.

"For African-American field workers, it was practically impossible to change their situation. The best they could hope for was a successful escape to the North. A German could break out of his confines—as the example of Matthias Hohner shows. A German could even legally leave the country, and emigrate to America. Millions grasped this opportunity in the nineteenth century. They either left behind political persecution or sought greater freedom of religious practice.

"The majority left, however, to escape from economic hardship, which was a recurring problem both in Trossingen—the region between the Black Forest on the West and the Swabian Alp to the East—and Klingenthal. It is well documented that in 1850 almost every Trossingen family had one relative in the New World. This was not much different in Klingenthal, from where in 1833 C. F. Martin, the founder of the famous guitar company, emigrated to Pennsylvania."

I began to study the other display cabinets. Arthur's collection was far from complete, but it contained all the major brands, with good examples of the basic styles from Richter diatonic (also called Haidaer, after the town Haida in Bohemia), of which the Marine Band became the most popular model in the United States; the Viennese or Tremolo, with its octave tuned reeds in separate holes that sound together if you blow or draw; the chord harmonica, pretty much restricted to accompaniment; and the chromatic harmonica where a slider on the mouth piece gives access to reed plates tuned a semitone apart, thereby allowing to easily play the full chromatic scale.

There were, for example, the Brass Band Harmonica with bells by Weiss, Trossingen; the submarine shaped U9 by Koch, Trossingen; a David's Harp from around 1900 with its harp-shaped resonating chamber and the Boomerang, both from Seydel; and Hohner's JazzBand, whose body reminded me of Siamese twins. I discovered a solid stock of Viennese manufactured instruments dating back to the first half of the nineteenth century that any museum would be proud to show. One had covers made of beautifully carved ivory, certainly a custom made piece for somebody who had a very distinctive taste and money to spend.

"Arthur often mentioned the fine work of early Austrian manufacturing." James remarked.

"That's right. Just look at those precious Thie instruments. The harmonica came indeed first to market in Vienna in the early 1820's. Ludwig van Beethoven must have seen one before he died in March 1827. Being deaf he will, however, have been spared from hearing what was described in Gathy's 'Musikalisches Conversations-Lexikon' of 1840 as 'a now customary playing style, and the most horrible thing for your ears.'"

"And when did it come to the United States?"

"As the instrument was so easily transportable, it certainly made its way across the Atlantic with the immigration waves from Europe around the middle of the 1800s at the latest."

"Will you join us at the funeral tomorrow morning?" Janice interrupted our meditation as we stood in front of displays of some lesser-known manufacturers, like Bilger, Brunnbauer, Eisen, Kalbe, Koch, and Pohl. I hadn't noticed her entering the room. "Service is at 10 a.m. at New Beginning United Free Will Baptist Church on King Avenue. We'll then go to the Mound City National Cemetery on Old 51 a few miles north from here."

I briefly thought of the road ahead and its vagueness versus the company and its certainty. I was under no time pressure. "When are you planning to go home tomorrow?"

Janice looked at James who had this blend of warmth, fascination and admiration on his face. His happiness increased when his mother replied, "We'll probably stay another night. There is so much to sort out. The will needs to be read. The sale of the house needs to be prearranged. There should be a real estate agent in the afternoon when we are back. Depending on the will, I may have to discuss with him what to do with this harmonica collection. I don't really have the full picture of all this now. Then, there are a couple of phone calls I rather make with Luther still around. Where are you staying for the night, Walter?"

"Where are *you* staying? Luther had suggested there might be an extra bed in the house, but I haven't even seen one bedroom so far. And I don't know. I did not bring my sleeping bag."

"Don't kid me you still have a sleeping bag! Your boy scout years are well over."

On the one hand that hurt and on the other hand I truly loved this directness from a non-German. My amazement must have shown for she seemed embarrassed. I asked, "You have any German blood in you? I mean this as a compliment. I really love your directness."

"You know I have actually been wondering. My hair was never quite as curly as that of my girlfriends. The farm where my forefathers worked as slaves in the Delta had a German owner for some fifty years. It could well be —" I smiled, knowing exactly what she was hinting at.

"There are two bedrooms on this floor and three more on the third floor," she added, "but I have booked myself into the hotel by the interstate exit."

She needed not to continue. More economical options were now only second best.

"Do you have their phone number? I'll try to get a room there, too."

James had gotten out of the chair and put all the

electronic equipment back in place.

"Can I switch off the lights, Walter?"

"Go ahead!" I said, knowing I would have another chance to admire the exhibit the next day.

Luther and Beth had just come up the landing with sleeping bags in hand, and carrying a suitcase to the end of the hall, where one bedroom must be. Luther looked over his shoulder, "I am happy to see that you are enjoying my family. I'm sure Janice convinced you to stay for the funeral. James will appreciate your harmonica expertise and your views about the Blues. I learned a lot from you." Beth was pulling him on. "Have you checked out the other bedrooms?"

"I have decided to stay at the hotel we passed, and I was just going to call."

"Darling, come on!" Beth said, kissing his earlobe.

"Good idea, see you tomorrow." Luther had just enough time to say before they disappeared into the room down the hall.

Luckily the hotel still had a vacancy and I confirmed the reservation by giving them my credit card.

More people, who I had not met came up the stairs with blankets for the night. I could not really imagine that everybody was going to bed, because it was still before 8 p.m. Luther was an exception; he apparently had particular obligations. The others would perhaps only arrange the beds and then come back down again. But when Janice, James and I looked around on the first floor, the dining table had been cleared, two full black garbage bags were waiting for us at the kitchen door, nobody was around and there was no indication this might change.

"Well," I thought, "this party is over and I haven't had a drop of alcohol."

"Walter, would you care for a night-cap?" Janice asked as I was wondering what to do next.

I had sort of suspected she was something special, but not that she could become my angel with one single sentence. "Since you ask, Janice, I wouldn't mind." I could barely conceal my excitement. I had no idea, where she would want to go—where one could go at all. If she had suggested to go back up the stairs to the private muse-um, and asked James to swing a secret bar to the front, in the same way he had shown me the vinyl records from the tunnel, I would not have been suprised. As my goddess, she could be sitting in the armchair, with me lying on the floor admiring the collage of her beautiful features with the harmonicas. But she apparently had a different idea.

"Come on, I'll lock the place. Some family mem-bers have driven from as far away as Detroit and Minne-apolis, and are dead tired." Shouting up the staircase, "Bye!" as we left.

I was sure that Luther did not pay attention nor give much of a damn. There was no response at all. The three of us were standing next to her car. "You won't need your car tonight. Grab what you need for the hotel."

I got my suitcase and the carry-on bag from the back seat. I did not want to leave anything visible in the car. In a way I was glad that James was of drinking age, in a way I was not sure it was the best idea that he was accompanying us.

"How you feeling, chaperon?" I teased him.

"How many grandchildren you said you have?" he shot back at me.

"Janice, where are we going?"

"There's a great Blues place over in Missouri, a well-kept secret even during the recent recession. It gives musicians from the area some space for live performances. People travel for two hours to hear their local stars. Sometimes an amazing White harper from Memphis comes by. Maybe we'll be lucky. They don't bother with a website. Have you ever been to Mississippi? The best stuff is hidden. I'm not talking about this alleged Faulkner quote rubbish 'To understand the world you have to understand a place like Mississippi'. I'm talking about how you need a local to show you where the music is."

I recalled having been in the capital, Jackson, once for a conference, and wanting to go out at night. Should I tell Janice about the underground bar, where I happened to join a private birthday party of a lady with her gigantic bottom squeezed in a too short and too tight orange skirt? I decided to leave that part out. "Yes, during a visit of Jackson I heard guitarist Jesse Robinson and his Legendary Friends. The mix of the audience was about ten per cent Whites, ninety per cent African-Americans. My friend told Jesse that I had brought my harps, and he invited me on stage to play along to a shuffle Blues.

"At that moment I felt for the first time what *Made in Germany–played in USA* truly meant. Martin Häffner, the director of the National Harmonica Museum in Trossingen, has written a book with this title. 'Harmonica and harmony' would have been a nice subtitle. But the house really started to rock when towards the end of the show this one-armed octogenarian joined the bandstand and sang *Bring it on home to me.*

> "Oh, you freely swinging reeds!
> Blow and draw rules apply.
> But for a harper to get by,
> you're really all he needs."

"Did you write that?" Janice asked. "I like it."

Chapter 5
Anyplace - where Blues is King

We drove for forty-five minutes, after first dropping our luggage at the hotel. When crossing the bridge over the Mississippi, I looked along the river to see if any barges were moving or had made fast along its shores, but it was already too dark. Janice was happy to play my CD with the cuts 1954 through 1960 from the Chess Blues box. I could not listen to CDs in my own car, as the beetle only had a cassette player.

My Babe with Little Walter always put me in a good mood, and another Willie Dixon track *Walking the Blues* had this unique beat resembling the slow ticking antique metronome I kept on my piano. Janice and James were also enjoying the music.

I was anxious to hear *Walking by Myself* by James A. Lane, also know as Jimmy Rogers. It had formed part of my early self-tutored trials on the harp. He was a Mississippian guitarist, vocalist and harmonicist who passed away in 1997 in Chicago aged seventy-three. The version I had first heard of that song was not the original, but the cover by the short-lived, grandiose all-white band Canned Heat. I had struggled in vain with some notes in the solo part of *On the Road Again* without ever getting them right. I needed Pat Missin on the web, just recently to find the solution to my riddle. He eloquently and comprehensibly explained that one needs to retune the sixth draw reed to get the missing G on the A harmonica. No wonder I couldn't get it right! I suspected that a genius on the instrument like Howard Levy would need no reed manipulation. From a regular diatonic—which, like any ten-hole harmonica only has nineteen obvious notes over three octaves—Howard gets more than all the thirty-six chromatic notes. With a diatonic, customized by another great player like Joe Filisko, even less experienced harmonicists might manage to play more than the easy-to-bend notes.

We entered a juke joint that looked like out of a 1950s movie—if only the Blues had already been credibly featured on celluloid in those years, which it sadly never was! A band was just wrapping up their set with early urban Blues stuff: guitar, e-bass, drums and harp.

The drummer was sitting idle. The harper, ending on the highest register, sounded exactly like Little Walter on the Jimmy Rogers song *Luedella* from 1950 that we had just heard in the car, played in second position on a D -harp, if I figured correctly. The harper was White, his baret sitting perfectly eschew. "Ladies and gentlemen, let's give Bill from Memphis a big hand!" The response was such that I assumed he had really impressed the forty or so patrons, some standing in front of the small stage where they had been dancing.

More people were gathered at the bar, but there were still a few empty stools. Janice arranged three together. We took our seats. James had to show his ID when he ordered a beer. I was reminded of the joyful feeling I had when I got drinks at the bar of a baseball stadium during a professional match only a few years earlier. The bartender's insistence on some form of ID—I know, of course, that it is only due to the fear of potential discrimination charges from others—had prompted me afterwards to have my own T-shirts printed, which I would wear from then on to every stadium visit. My three favorite slogans were "Thanks for asking! You made Grandpa so happy!," "You are absolutely right! I am wearing a mask!" and "Are you suggesting I am *past* drinking age? Tell my lawyer."

Bill came to the bar and stood next to me. "Great playing, man. Can I buy you a drink? What make do you use?" I asked.

"Thanks, I'll have a beer. I only play Hohner's *Golden Melody*. You play?"

"A little. I am a more of a theorizer."

"What you theorizing about?"

"The German background of the instrument and its success story in the United States; the history of the harmonica Blues created by the African-Americans; the role of the harmonica in extending the life span of Blues which is far greater than its pocket size suggests; its rebound across the Atlantic in the '60s, while it temporarily disappeared from sight in the United States; and the harmonica's current presence in instruction classes on the web and its revival here, with eventual greater consciousness about German craftsmanship."

"Sounds serious, man. I sure hope you're not missing out on the fun part of it."

"If I did, I wouldn't be here. When is your next set? These are my friends, Janice and James, by the way. I'm Walter." We clinked our bottles.

"Bill is my name as you heard. We're easy. I don't think before fifteen minutes." He took a sip. "To be honest, I always thought Hohner or Seydel, but never German harmonica. Tell me more."

"I am trying to build a bridge between the work ethos, the conservatism and the traditional musical taste that Matthias Hohner embodied until his death in 1902 and the exploration and use of his main product and major export article to the United States by the earliest Blues musicians at around the same time. I'm afraid Matthias would have turned over in his grave, rotating like helicopter blades and quickly arisen to ask for asylum in German folk harmonica heaven, had he been aware of the very successful attempts in the American South to substitute the human voice with the harmonica. The build and the bendability of its reeds, which I consider the instrument's soul, lend themselves much easier than other wind instruments to an imitation of whining or moaning vocal sounds. The slave had no voice in politics, economics and other determining factors of his existence, but he had a voice to sing.

"As it were, his voice was one of the few possessions that could not be easily taken away from him. The slave-owners could always restrict the place and the time of the singing, and the slave would know that the articulation of critical views and complaints about his condition was not permissible. But, as long as the singing increased the productivity of work in the cotton-fields, it was allowed. After the emancipation of the Negro in 1865, new opportunities for using their voice in a social context arose. They could be explored even in the South, until the Reconstruction came to an end in 1877 and new forms of repression took eventually over in the form of the infamous Jim Crow laws since 1890.

"This was possibly the formative period of the close relationship between the German harmonica and the American Blues that continues until today. It is difficult to prove my point, as there are no recordings of harmonica Blues from before the 1920s, only sound documents of fox chase and the train. So we have to put up with many unknowns for the fifty-year gap since the 1870s. But, as far as political sympathies go, I know more examples of

outspoken support by German immigrants for the aboli-
tion of slavery than of support for continued segregation.
Together with their progressive attitude—take for example the Giessen Immigration Society in Missouri or Carl
Schurz—German harmonicas in the mouth of the first
Bluesmen are for me a symbol of solidarity and friendship
that transcends music.

"I have no doubt that the harmonica came to the
United States in limited quantities in the pockets of European immigrants since it was manufactured on a small
scale in Vienna, Trossingen, Klingenthal and Graslitz.
Although there are no known paintings or photos from the
Civil War showing the harmonica, it was already in the
country at that time. If you believe in the historical truth
of Hollywood movies, there is a scene in Szelnik's *Gone
With the Wind* that depicts a band of musicians celebrat-
ing the end of the Civil War, one of whom plays a harmonica. Be that as it may, the first visit to Trossingen by a
U.S. wholesale supplier looking for harmonicas is recorded for 1865! Can you believe that?

"And the connection between American watch-
making technologies and the production of watches in
Switzerland and the Black Forest in the mid 1850s is fascinating. You know, Matthias Hohner was a watch-ma—"

The intermission was shorter than expected. The
drummer had been gesturing to Bill for a while and Janice
touched my shoulder.

"Man, this is amazing, but I've got to get back on stage. Nice listening to you. Thanks for the beer." He was off.

"Can *you* speak!" Janice exploded. "Like a book. Have you learned that by heart?" Gasping, but now much calmer, she added, "Sorry, I found that really very interesting. I guess most people don't have the faintest idea."

"I got carried away."

"No, I really mean it."

"I agree." James added.

At the bandstand, the next set had begun with some R & B. I hesitated, but, yes, it was *Every Day I Have the Blues* sounding like a blend of the B. B. King and Eric Clapton versions. Bill playing full throttle gave us something like the entire brass section. It was even better. The whole place was pretty packed now. The sound level was such that you couldn't think of a conversation. Also, the music was simply too good.

They slowed down song after song. With their tenth piece, Janice grabbed my hand and drew me to the dance floor. Another song made famous by B. B., *The Thrill Is Gone*. We moved in a way that contradicted the title. What happened? I looked into her understanding eyes and felt out of this world. No chance to signal good-bye to the harper who had put up a great performance. She pulled me away past the bar where James seemed to have been expecting our move.

"That was real nice." she whispered in my ear on the way to her car. James was walking awkwardly by our side. My theorizing had made me tired and I yawned loudly. "Excuse me, but I think I talked too much."

What a day lay behind me! I had been on my butt with the foot on the gas for six hours.

Lots of new faces. A drive of almost one hour each way to and from the juke joint. Time for bed. We had the two front windows down and listened only to the wind and the noise of our car and others passing us. The beautiful live music still reverberated in our heads. It deserved to be preserved as was. James had fallen asleep on the back seat, and had to be woken up as we parked in front of the hotel. As we approached our rooms, I briefly thought of spooning as the perfect end of the day. But this was so cliché. I gently stroked Janice's left cheek with the back of my hand before I briefly kissed her on the other and wished her and James a good night.

Chapter 6
Arthur's funeral

I was dreaming of the famous funeral scene in the James Bond film *Live And Let Die*. I was the spectator with the hat who got stabbed in the right side of my belly, so I never got to listen to the up-tempo part of the New Orleans brass band. I was so mad about missing out that I forced myself to go through various repeats of the same scene. Then I decided that I did not accept my own death, especially not that inexplicable disappearance of the body under the coffin as if it was sucked up. Actually, that lack of logical explanation of how the body got off the street helped me to deconstruct the whole scene and declare it as an absurdity that I would never want to be part of. The guy who killed me had suddenly no longer a knife, but he was Oskar Matzerath of Günther Grass' novel *Tin Drum*. He held drumsticks in his hands and shrieked so loud that the band took that as a signal to drop the coffin and fall into their fast rhythm immediately. I held my ears while I ran to where the marching band was headed and waited for them clapping every other beat. Oskar had not broken any glass, because there was none in those old houses.

"Wait a minute," I thought, as I awoke sweating heavily, happy to be alive, but instantaneously questioning my sanity. It was three o'clock in the morning and I felt very lonely.

Eventually I must have fallen asleep again, because a loud pounding noise on the door brought me back. "Walter, are you okay? We're getting breakfast." James shouted.

"Give me a couple of minutes. I just woke up." My sheets were damp. I skipped shaving and went straight into the shower. The sun was in my room, so it must be past eight.

Dark blue cotton pants and an off-white dress shirt were the best alternative to tons of denims and tees in my suitcase and I chose them. No tie. I would surely be underdressed, at least for the slow first movement of the procession. But, going on a field trip to explore the land of the Blues, should one be prepared for every possible occasion including funerals? I later observed that my dress code considerations were unnecessary. Absolutely nobody made me feel out of place.

"Good morning." Janice said, when I knocked on her door ten minutes later. "Sleep well?"

"So-so, I dreamt of New Orleans or 'Nawlins', as you say," I simplified my nightmare.

"Nothing wrong with 'Nawlins' as you allege we

say. Let's get coffee up on Old 51. That's already on the way to the cemetery, and we have to go south again to the funeral service in Cairo before that. But, I can't help it. I don't know a decent place in town!"

Fixing breakfast at the house with Luther and the rest would have made much more sense. I had seen at least a Dollar Central somewhere the day before. Why should I, however, interfere with the planning and the proceedings. Simply drifting along was nice for a change. On the way to the parking lot I stopped by the reception and asked them to hold my room for another night.

After about one mile we pulled up in front of a roadside cafe. Somehow, it was no surprise being greeted by family members who were already enjoying a full breakfast. Luther called from the far end of the room, pointing at two still vacant seats. He pulled his wife even closer, making room for James on the bench beside him. In my direction: "How is harmonikaizer doing this morning?"

"Can I take that as a compliment?"

"Sure, isn't kaizer the German word for emperor?"

"Like kaizer roll over Beethoven!"

"Your puns are good, but complicated." Janice commented, ordering regular coffee with the waitress at the same time. "You're out of what? Egg powder?"

"We weren't prepared for such an invasion." the waitress replied.

"Okay, French toast, then." Janice said.

I asked for a muffin and cappuccino. "Only coffee, regular or decaf." was the answer. "Then regular, please." I replied.

The conversation at the other tables was as usual: baseball, football, basketball—though some of them off-season—and the weather. Through the densely woven carpet of voices I could distinguish the high pitch of a stocky lady in her forties who must be in a dispute with her teen daughter, I suspected. I had noticed her slightly hysterical and too loud tone the evening before. Beth was not the only shrill woman.

"That's Roberta," Beth remarked. "She's giving Alicia a hard time again."

"Maybe it's the other way round," Luther indicated where his sympathies lay in this matter.

"These are the moments when I'm glad we have no kids."

"Oh, come on," Beth stroked his hair.

"Inhale, exhale, inhale, exhale and circular breathing," I thought when the crescendo continued to build. A harmonica would need amplification to be heard above the noise. An accordion might still cope, and the effect on the group of a cacophonic chord with the left hand on all the reachable buttons and the right hand playing trills in the highest register would interest me.

There had been a delay in the coffee brewing. Some of us became impatient. My muffin was gluey. Even the tongue acrobatics that harpers are used to, didn't help. Water was the only remedy.

"We'll be late for the service unless we get going *now*!" Luther shouted. A general commotion followed. Twenty or so chairs were being shoved—we were more people, but some had not found seats. Money was counted and left on the tables.

Nobody waited for the waitress to come by. All figured out their own account. In less than three minutes we sat in our cars. It was 9:55 a.m. The convoy raced off. Future City was honored with lightning speed. When we turned onto Dr. Martin Luther King Drive we could see from the distance the deacons standing at the curb and then rushing inside the church.

The front of First Beginning Free Will Baptist Church reminded me of a larger version shotgun house that I had seen in books on the South, and which I expected to see in great numbers in Mississippi during my trip. "A dying community and one of how many churches?" I thought. We were five minutes late, but as we constituted the entire congregation the delay didn't matter at all. Arthur showed eternal patience in his coffin with a nice white flower decoration.

Two male members asked a deacon where the restroom was, apparently leading to some unplanned preparations behind the scenes, which provoked three women to follow. The "hush, hush" from an elderly lady—"Aunt Agathy from St. Louis," as Janice whispered—did not make much of an impression. The pastor had not yet appeared. I was in good company without jacket and tie. Luther and Beth to my left were checking their smartphones.

"Could I borrow one for a minute?" I asked. Luther passed me his. The internet signal was miserable. I had entered "Churches in Cairo, Illinois" in the search function and the wheel kept turning, turning. Finally, coinciding with the pastor stepping out, it showed a list of thirteen. It proved my rule of thumb that any town with a minimum of 1,000 inhabitants would have around ten different denominations. During the opening hymn—I forget what it was—another figure came up as result of my search for the church I was sitting in. According to this, there were still over 3,000 people living in Cairo. Where were Arthur's neighbors hiding?

The pastor was officiating nicely. But I didn't pay attention to detail. My mind had drifted away to Arthur's treasure cabinet and the untold stories behind the instruments, their makers and players. In the eulogy only brief mention was made of Arthur as a collector. Mostly, it was his service to his country that the pastor dwelled upon, a recurring theme in this land that cultivated heroism. Why then was he not buried at Arlington or on another national cemetery? I knew he had the right. Arthur must have had his reasons. I hoped I would remember to ask about that.

Janice pushed an open hymnbook in my hand. I sang along to *Forever with the Lord*. Finally, there it was: I was overwhelmed with the intensity, the soulfulness and the beauty of the ad hoc multi voice rendition. What a difference from the rational timidity that characterized communal singing in the church of my youth in Germany! This passion—although neither "passion" nor "fervor" quite captured the *Inbrunst* I sensed—was much more to my liking.

"Your voice isn't bad. Are you crying?" Janice whispered as I closed the hymnbook.

"It's moving. I like it."

Janice tapped on my hand as my mind started drifting again. Eighty-four years filled with a life that I knew nothing about except for a name, a military rank, the last residence, a hobby, family members who had temporarily been closely interwoven with it and who were the accidental connection. The ceremony proceeded and I experienced how different layers of consciousness began to overlap. I was hallucinating various screens on the white walls of the simple church interior. The capitalized headline B. B. KING IS DEAD appeared. Below this I read: Visit his museum in Indianola and his birthplace! Next to these sentences appeared the huge imposing figure of Howlin' Wolf, born fifteen years before the King. The next minute he was young, sitting under a Christmas tree, proudly showing his annual present, a German harmonica for twenty-five cents. One screen showed the constantly flashing face of Arthur.

Around him trucks were coming and going, dumping hundreds of thousands of harmonicas. When the pile had reached a certain height, a giant arm wiped it off the screen. My sensitivity had reached a point where I could hear the instruments crashing on the tiles of the church floor. "What a sacrifice!" I thought. Then my old primary school teacher spoke to me: "Don't you know, Walter, that harmonica reeds wear out like guitar strings? What else should people do with the no longer usable pieces? Put them under their pillows? Ha, foolish boy!"

As his mocking laughter faded, I wanted to answer that I knew very well: "Replacement parts were not customary until a generation ago—Hohner started a modular system only in the 1990s." I opened my mouth to say in emotionless staccato: "I have studied my lesson, teacher. The limited life span of a single instrument explains the huge volumes that were shipped to the United States in the decade before the Great Recession. Hohner alone sold twenty million of them in the United States in 1925. The Twenties were roaring also for the harmonica manufacturers." But I couldn't speak. Next to the harmonica dump— was the giant swiping arm a symbol of the denial of metal recycling or of the instrument's rejection by influential social circles that ridiculed it as a toy?—endless streams of African-Americans threw down their rural tools, and reappeared in the steel-mills of Gary and the slaughter houses of Chicago. Then the Wolf came on again, he cupped his hands around the tiny thing, howled and said: "I did not move to Chicago until 1953 and stayed until my death in 1976."

People around me started getting up. The coffin was carried past us out of the front door to a black hearse. I was a little disappointed that there was no Nawlins Jazz band.

"You were really daydreaming again." James said.

"Did I talk?"

"No, you didn't, but your open eyes told stories. I wished I could have understood them."

I accompanied Janice and James to the hearse where other family members touched the coffin for a last time. Standing beside them I continued with my reflections, this time aloud:

"The harmonica is a throw-away instrument. Is there a future for the Blues after it has lost its role as the valve for the release of pain and identifier of a community? Are its survival chances greater as a musical genre only? Or is the Blues chapter closed for good when the great singers, harpers and guitarists are gone? Whereas complex and elaborate compositions, from violin or piano sonatas to whole orchestral works and operas define their quality on paper, the quality of the Blues lies solely in the execution by the musician. The rendition rises far above the simple musical idea. Being part of an oral versus a written tradition, the Blues depends less on the reproducibility of fixed notes than on the capability of the artist to create it."

"Are these not artificial and unnecessary distinctions?" Janice commented as the coffin disappeared and the back door of the hearse was closed. "I think, music as culture and genre always go together. Baroque music died with the Bachs and classical music exhausted itself after Beethoven. As you just explained, they were the creators of different musical styles in different historical periods just like the composers and painters of romanticism, impressionism and expressionism later. Yet, still today people listen to the music, play it, record it."

She was directing me towards her parked car and handed James the keys: "You mind driving? I can concentrate better on this conversation."

I took a seat in the back. Why was she half-hearted and sat in the front? It would have made much more sense to join me on the back seat instead of contorting her upper body from the front passenger seat to face me and force me to sit behind James. He knew the car well and eased into his space in the convoy, as it slowly started moving towards the cemetery.

"I mostly agree. But if the Blues depends so much on its authentic interpreters, I worry that we might not be able to preserve it when they are gone. If you trust W. C. Handy, the 'Father of the Blues' as he is called, it appeared around 1900. So it can already look back to a proud history of over 110 years."

"Which is phenomenal compared to other musical styles! The original musicians will eventually all be gone. But the music will survive—thanks also to your harmonica. Trust me."

"I may be hopelessly nostalgic," I admitted, "but the point I wanted to make is simply the following: I had this hallucination that B. B. King died—"

"Not yet," James eyed me through the rearview mirror, "but before the church service I read a news report that his condition was getting worse, and that he would most likely not be able to ever go back on tour again."

"B. B.'s time will come or has come. To pass I mean. He is a human being after all. As a musician he has missed the time for a graceful exit already. I saw one of his concerts in New England last year and I left after the second title he played. He stood clearly beside himself.

"The reeds and brass were out of tune—but that's another story. The crowd in the packed hall—who certainly meant well—cheered him on to sing *You Are My Sunshine*, which he then started and didn't stop for fifteen minutes. To me these minutes seemed like an eternity. I felt he was being abused. He could no longer get his musical message across. He was practically raped on stage by fans whose benevolence I don't question. But, did they appreciate to what extent he truly was the Blues? The pain of what I think is the greatest humiliation that can happen to a musician, became unbearable for me, and I had to get out. The next day, I learned B. B. had played a few riffs of the next song and then been escorted offstage. His manager should be punished for keeping him touring!"

"What if B. B. was the one who did not want to quit?"

"There is a point in everybody's life after which you must be protected from yourself. When you begin to destroy your reputation, your family or friends must then take the necessary measures."

"What if he needed the money?"

"To feed his fifteen or so illegitimate children? To pay for his musicians and their families? I understand, he cared a lot for others. Was Howlin' Wolf the only responsible bandleader who took out social security for his people? Is this a systemic problem of the United States or of capitalism in general? B. B. King was a very successful musician. He worked hard. He must have generated enough income for long stretches of his career from performances, publication rights, royalties. Were Blues musicians compensated so much worse than Pop or Rock stars?"

I felt that I was asking too many questions. I wasn't sure whether I had been clear enough in my attempt to talk about the Blues as an endangered species that needed to be saved. But the attention of my company in the car was rather encouraging. They had been all ears till we reached the cemetery, where a brief burial ceremony took place.

Chapter 7
Back in the treasure chamber

All sentimentalities ceased after Arthur's coffin was lowered into the ground. The more distant relatives started their homeward journey directly from the cemetery. Three cars, including Janice's and Luther's, made their way back to the house. The real estate agent had confirmed to be there at 2 p.m., the executor of the will was supposed to come at 3 p.m. Arthur had named an old friend from the local fire department, who had been at church, but could not make it to the cemetery.

I had nothing to do with these indispensable formalities, though I was curious to know at least who might inherit the instrument collection. While the family waited downstairs, James had reopened the museum for me, and as I fell into the comfy chair, it took me only a few glimpses at the earliest models to forget about my current place and time. I recalled what people had told me, and what I had read about life in the mid nineteenth century in Western Saxony bordering on Bohemia or between the

Black Forest and the Swabian Alp. While I was recalling this information I became an active participant of that history.

I *existed* around 1850 in a rural German environment, whose conservative orientation was an obstacle to cultural or business ambitions—*lived* would be a euphemism compared with today's comforts. I would get up at dawn to tend my cow and the small plot of mediocre soil I had inherited. Neither was I as bad off as the many marginalized poor of the village, nor did I belong to the substantial number of rich farmers or to the small industrious middle class of crafts– or tradesmen. My condition was better than that of the sharecropper in the American South after the Civil War, because I owned my land.

The risk of accumulating new debts at the end of every year was high, if the yield of the land turned out to be far less than expected, and the loan taken out for seed and equipment could not be paid back. I still felt the after-effects of the European agricultural crisis of 1846/7, when the famine had driven people to emigrate, many of them to the United States. I could also easily top up my income by investing time in additional productive activity. Many neighbors in similar conditions tried to generate income with cottage work. Weaving had been a possibility until steam-powered machines replaced manual labor. But supplying parts to clock or musical instrument manufacturing still offered opportunities. The winter months were best for this, as the cold weather reduced agricultural chores or brought them to a standstill altogether. On the other hand, work by candlelight was extremely strenuous for my eyes and the quality standards of the manufacturer, to whom I delivered my pieces, were high. Assembly of the parts took place at the house of the master craftsman who—if successful—might become the founder of a company and director of a factory.

I counted myself among this group of lucky entrepreneurs and focused on musical instruments. Climbing up the social ladder included getting married. And, as was common, my wife would not only cook for the family, but also for our apprentices. Good business instinct, combined with organizational talent and fine-motor skills facilitated a steady progress towards full-scale pre-industrial manufacturing under my own expanding roof. Instrument parts, built according to precise instructions, were now delivered to *my* doorstep, among them the cover plates, the wooden combs—no alternative to wood for the comb existed at the time—and the reed plates. I focused on the reeds themselves, which were hammered out from brass threads, then milled and filed. The secret of the sound lay in the alloy, I soon knew. I had different workstations to attach the reeds to the reed plates and the plates to the comb. Before affixing the cover to the comb, a worker with a good ear checked the tuning of the reeds, so that it could be corrected without having to remove the covers.

As demand grew, we moved from the kitchen into the larger hall, and eventually added another building. Af ter successfully passing through the cottage worker stage, the agricultural component of my income was no longer essential. But, I would certainly encourage my workers to keep this emergency backup. And even I would continue to appreciate a small piece of cultivated land as a stabilizing element in economic downturns and times of need.

My story was typical of German harmonica makers.

Across the Atlantic, the instruments we had produced would themselves become means of production for musicians, among them the Blues people. The harmonica belonged to the small group of instruments used for entertaining parties. The time they invested in this type of creativity outside of their normal workplace helped them to get an extra meal and moonshine, if lucky, even some welcome cash.

I felt a touch on my shoulder. James stood by the chair, in which I had fallen fast asleep.

"You know what? Mother and uncle Luther inherited the house and guess—"

"You got the movables in this room, the instrument collection, the vinyl records and the electronic equipment!" I completed his sentence, although having barely returned to the present.

"Yeah, and you know what's even better? There must be a suitcase hidden behind a panel in the record compartment. I got the key here."

He opened the drawer and pushed the button to set the mechanism for the record player in motion. When everything was in place he reached inside to feel the interior panel.

"I don't feel a handle." He knocked on the panel. It sounded like there was a hollow space behind it.

"Softly go along the frame edge with your index finger. I'm sure you'll find a lever somewhere or a hole."

He did as I advised.

"There is something at the bottom, but I can't move it sideways."

"Let me see." I loved this. Luther, Beth and Janice were standing in the doorway watching. I shifted my position in the chair to reach over and found a wedge that could be pushed down. I pulled my hand back fast, because at that moment a spring behind the panel pushed it forward. It slid to the front so that one could grab it at the top where a sufficient opening had formed. After taking the panel out, James lifted out an attaché case from the cabinet.

"It's clean and quite heavy. I don't think it has been sitting here for long. Otherwise we would find dust, spider webs or what have you." James remarked.

"Put it on this high table where Arthur used to

show and explain his harmonica beauties to us visitors." Janice suggested.

James unlocked the suitcase with his key and opened it. On top was a handwritten letter by Arthur to James, signed with a date barely 3 months ago.

"My dear grandson James,

"As you read this letter, it gives me great joy and comfort that you have not declined my bequest. I'm watching from above—this may sound boisterous, but there are so many worse guys than I was, and hell must be overcrowded, so I'm confident to end up in heaven—and enjoying your surprise in checking the content of this case. I trust that you will apply wisdom and the managerial skills that your MBA degree attests when taking a decision about using what I call a true treasure. It is not only the instruments that I have loved for their particular German-American history, and the music that our people played on them.

"Their immaterial value is far higher than their material value. But, if you desperately need money, there is this or that piece that will easily get you a couple of hundred bucks on eBay. The Viennese ivory harmonicas from the 1850s are worth far more. And you will recall that I mentioned some harmonicas that were played by famous harpers. There are three Marine Bands that Howlin' Wolf, Sonny Boy Williamson II and Carey Bell played. You will find letters signed by them with original photos of their instrument that are clearly marked with initials on the covers.

"I will have no control over all this after I am gone, but I trust you identify enough with what was more than a hobby for me after your grandmother had passed. So, I have high hopes that you will not easily part with all this. As you have just graduated, and I cannot burden you financially, you will find a stack of fifty 100-dollar bills in an envelope. That should be plenty for a couple of years storage space rental, before you get your own house or apartment. There is more valuable stuff in this suitcase, including some original documents like letter exchanges of Hohner, Seydel and other manufacturers from the late nineteenth century with American importers or German exporters to the United States, catalogues of the World Fairs in Philadelphia 1876, New Orleans 1884, Chicago 1893, Omaha 1898, Buffalo 1901, St. Louis 1904 and a few brochures by participating German harmonica makers; mail order catalogues of Montgomery Ward and Sears Roebuck from the 1890s. You will find the original American document establishing the U.S. consular agency in Markneukirchen near Klingenthal that existed from 1893 until 1916, and which played a major role in expediting instrument exports to the United States, not only from Klingenthal, but also from Trossingen and many other places in Europe.

"I am sure you will appreciate that, notwithstanding your acceptance of the bequest, my last will clearly stipulates one condition for you finally taking over the reponsibility for the collection: Before you dump, give away or sell any of the contents in this room, you must first use the attached open dated business class ticket to visit the Trossingen and Zwota museums as well as the Hohner and Seydel factories. As you have never been to Europe before, this will give you what I consider a necessary education above your degree.

"I loved seeing you grow up. Your curiosity in my passion has always been a great inspiration for me to keep going. Make the best of your life. I hope this collection will contribute to your success!

"Your loving Grandpa"

"What a letter!" all of us exclaimed simultaneously. James had tears in his eyes. "I can't go through the rest of the stuff now." he said. "I'm also very hungry." It was 6 p.m. and we had not had anything serious for lunch.

"Sure!" To my surprise, it was Beth who answered enthusiastically, revealing her Louisiana background. "I can fix us some easy soul food in no time if you like grits for dinner. There's plenty of it and spices are left in the kitchen. They should have some catfish or at least chicken at the Dollar market. I'll get it. You can stay, Luther."

"I'm curious to see how they are stocked. I may have been too negative in my comments to Walter about Cairo yesterday. They even have this new hotel where you guys are staying. I'll come with you." Luther said. They left.

"I can understand your emotions, but if you need some translation of any German writings, it is easier with me still being around." I said.

"You're right." James had regained his composure. "Why don't we take the attaché case to the dining room?"

"Before we go: Did Arthur ever tell you the story behind that instrument?" I pointed to a prominently dis-played tremolo harmonica from the 1910s that was badly twisted and had what looked like a little funnel in its side.

"Oh, sure! Don't pretend not to know what it is! That harmonica's history was one of his favorite conversa-tion issues. I actually don't see the bullet, which belongs in the hole. For some time it lay next to the harp. Arthur said he knew the guy. It was some infantryman from this area who had fought in 1917 in Europe, after the United States entered the First World War. Grandpa explained there were many similar cases of soldiers being saved by harmonicas in their breast pockets. I don't know whether he invented this story, but once he voiced suspicion that a large number of these lifesavers on flea markets must be fakes by Dutch or Polish antique dealers."

I burst out laughing. Not even the American South was immune to typical European prejudices. James smiled and then turned more serious.

"One remark I will never forget. We were discussing senseless gang killings in cities like Chicago. He said it was too bad that campaigns to spread harmonica teaching in schools, when there were more than 150 harmonica youth orchestras in Chicago, had not been sustainable. If schoolkids carried the harp in the right spot, mortality might be reduced."

"Good point on a very sad subject. Yet, being a harper with more than one instrument on him did not prevent William McKinley 'Jazz' Gillum from being shot dead in 1966." I commented.

Downstairs in the kitchen, Janice easily found the right sized pot, mixed in the packet of grits with water from the tap and put it on the stove. The further ingredients could be stirred in later. James started to meticulously arrange the different stacks of documents at the far end of the dining table, leaving plenty of space for the five of us at the other end. He reshuffled the papers over and over after studying anew the short descriptions of the various folders. I found plates and cutlery and began to set the table. James was about done as Beth and Luther returned. They had not even been away fifteen minutes.

"Surprise, surprise!" she chirped and lifted two bottles of Chilean chardonnay wine out of the brown bag, followed by some bread rolls, butter, oil, fresh cilantro, ham and ice cream.

"It's more or less as I expected." Luther remarked.

"It wasn't so bad. There was frozen catfish and frozen shrimps. But we thought it would take too long to defrost." Beth defended the market offerings. "See, the wine is even cold! Thanks, Janice, let me take over. James, why don't you open a bottle and pour us some?"

"I'll do it. He's busy." I was happy to jump in. The bottle had a convenient screw cap and in a minute everybody held a full glass. "To Arthur!"

Luther had sat down on the sofa with a newspaper. Beth was at the stove. Janice watched over James's shoulder as he was trying to make sense of a German book titled *Matthias Hohner. Leben und Werk*, by an author named Lämmle.

"I have heard that Matthias Hohner was the man who founded the factory, but what do the other words mean?"

"*Life and Achievements*. 'Werk' is etymologically the same as 'work', but the meaning of it is wider in this context. There is one very funny anecdote in Lämmle's book. In 1857 Matthias Hohner tried to sell his first batch of six mouth organs, which clearly were not up to the sound purity of other makes on the market. Back home, very disappointed, his wife suggested he should send them to a cousin in Canada, where the quality standards would not be so high.

"She was right. In Canada they sold without a

problem. Isn't that nice? The anecdote highlights three important aspects: the influential and strong position of Anna Hohner in the family business, a certain disdain for family members who had emigrated, and the bumpy start of Hohner's business. James, especially you, as you look for a job now, can find a lot of encouragement in this. Don't give up easily if you experience failure. After all, Hohner became the greatest harmonica manufacturer of the world."

"I'm sorry I don't speak German."

"You can still learn it."

"Look at this!" James pulled a heavily used booklet titled *German for Beginners* from an envelope. "Ma, did you know that Grandpa tried to learn German?"

"Yes, but he was too embarrassed by his pronunciation—"

I thought: "What a serious learner! I would have liked the guy. Normally, Americans pronounce every foreign word as if it were of American English origin."

"I believe his reading and passive knowledge were more than rudimentary." Janice continued. "Wasn't he convinced his basic German helped him get that remarkable trade deal in Klingenthal in '89?"

"No, I don't remember. What's this?" James showed me a catalog.

After some scrutiny, I was excited that the new find might even predate the earliest Hohner catalog from 1890/91 held in the museum archives in Trossingen. "This has true historical value, I guess."

Next, James discovered the handwritten letters by Howlin' Wolf, Sonny Boy Williamson II and Carey Bell. They dated from 1974, 1963 and 2005, which interestingly in each case was two years before their respective deaths. Only the last one by Bell was directed to Arthur, the other two carried the addresses of unknown people. Arthur had clipped a little note to both, stating when, which flea market and, at what price he had acquired them. I could not think of Carey Bell without having a clear picture of his friendly big face and his terrible teeth in front of me; the same with Walter Horton and James Cotton. The latter could still be asked, how he lost his teeth, if I had the chance to ever meet him. I guess none of these guys had any insurance and not enough money to invest in their handsomeness. Amazing that the huge gaps in their front teeth did not negatively impact Carey's and James's harp playing.

"Almost ready!" Beth shouted across the room. The smell of the ham, slowly fried in a pan, drifted over from the stove. Rolls and butter were already on the table. Luther had left the sofa and sat in a dinner chair. James took the seat next to him.

"Luther, have you ever studied German?"

"I took a class and then switched to French. I thought for TV-ad production and with the proximity to Canada that would be more useful. I don't know. I have never really had any chance for business up north."

Beth brought the big pot of grits to the table. The ham was already mixed with it. It was nicely garnished with the cilantro.

"Speaking of Canada, anybody for maple syrup?"

I shuddered.

"Ketchup? No? What's wrong with you guys?" Beth sat down at the head of the table. Janice next to me offered to serve and I passed her my plate. I liked the smell, and apparently Beth had not poured the frying fat over the grits, only the ham itself, so it was not greasy. Luther suggested that grace be said, as this was a special day, Arthur's funeral and most likely the last family meal in his house. He briefly thanked for the full life that the deceased had enjoyed, and his self-discipline that permitted the generations around the table to benefit from his material goods. He prayed for Arthur's soul, asked for the food to be blessed and for safe travels for those who had returned to their homes and those who would leave the next day.

We toasted to the chef. Beth had really not promised too much. The simple dish was deliciously prepared, the grits just the right consistency, not too liquid, not too dry, the ham just bringing out its best taste, the spices delicately applied. A pinch of extra salt was all I needed. Surprisingly, nobody spoiled the meal with the sauces Beth had ironically suggested. Despite her shrillness I had developed a strong sympathy for her and felt I understood Luther's devotion better.

"So, you plan to write a book after this trip? Do you have a title yet? Do you think anybody is interested in the connection between the harmonica and the Blues? Will we be in it?" "That's a lot of questions, James." I replied. "Yes, I plan to interweave fiction with as many historically accurate facts as possible. The title should somehow mention the instrument and the musician, but my main concern is to find a publisher. I strongly believe it is a story for many readers. My approach is new in that it tries to combine information about German harmonica manufacturers, the American attraction to the harmonica, important harpers and the history of the Blues, with current socio-political developments. To the many points I made last night at the jukejoint I could add: Is there a particular reason why the African-American discovered the hidden qualities of the harmonica, especially the full chromatic scale in the low register? Since when does a direct connection between the manufacturer and Blues musicians exist? I hope to introduce the reader to the complexities of this small instrument and show that it is a true giant. And, finally, yes, you will all be in it. But, you may not recognize yourselves. I'll make every effort to protect your true identities."

"We're not afraid. I hope I didn't snore when I dozed off during your lecture before the Cairo exit." Luther said with a big smile on his face.

"How could I write anything ugly after your friendship, great hospitality and especially this delicious meal? I have felt at home ever since I set foot in this house."

"Did you tell Janice and James that we were stopped by the police? Beth loved the story."

"Actually, we didn't have time for that."

Luther did not wait for a show of hands, but as soon as he had started it was obvious that James and Janice were excited to hear the rest. He spun the story like a slowly developing harmonica solo in the style of Ravel's Bolero. He obviously enjoyed demonstrating his skills as a narrator, not particularly minding how sailor's yarn gained the upper hand over facts. In between, he took many sips from his wine glass that was immediately refilled by James. His embellishments of my invented explanation to the cops why I was driving Luther, and his mimicking of their final send-off were hilarious and kept us rocking in our chairs. Then Janice told one of her experiences with the police, which also sounded a lot funnier than it must have been at the time. With the years, the story had lost its oppressiveness and was reduced to an improvised comedy around the family dining table.

"Are we all done?" It was a rhetorical question. As Beth could see that pot and plates were empty. "What about some dessert? I found a bottle of aged rum in the cupboard over the sink. You can have it with or without banana ice cream."

"Would you, please, stop that!" I demanded in jest in Janice's direction as she gave me this you-will-certainly -go-for-rum-only look. I suspected this was because of my nightcap craving the previous night. Luther was too late to prevent James from pouring him the final content of the second bottle of wine. The dessert question was pragmatically solved by putting bowls and brandy glasses with the rum and a quarter gallon pot of ice cream in the middle of the table.

"I love banana ice!" I stated emphatically.

"Did many harpers drink?" James asked. "As far as I know heavy drinking was a problem for quite a few." I replied. "Given their environment—both where they came from and where they worked as musicians—they all made the acquaintance with alcohol, or with moonshine, at some time. Rhythm Willie died a heavy drinker in 1945 at around forty-five—his birthday and birthplace are obscure. Sonny Boy Williamson I became aggressive when he had too much booze, his namesake number II drank, so did Howlin' Wolf, Junior Wells and Jimmy Reed. Muddy Waters, at the height of his career, was regularly depicted with his champagne. He needs to be mentioned, because he started off as a harper, then switched to guitar and at a later stage allegedly questioned, whether he should not have better stuck to his harmonica. Although singing the praise of the harmonica, I'm glad he didn't. But, abuse and drugs were not exclusive to harmonica players. Don't misunderstand me. Neither do I mean they were particularly bad. Jazzers post World War II were probably more into drugs. And, many other artists in the music industry are in the habit. It's a sad fact."

"Where do you plan do go tomorrow?" Janice inquired. "Having so much information already from reading, what is the purpose of visiting places?"

"I would like you to help me with some final details, if you don't mind. It's basically the Mississippi Delta I want to see. There are great harpers from other areas in the United States, but to me the Delta seems like the epicenter. Reading about and experiencing live are totally different processes in our brain and give us different insights and emotions. Sometimes the Wi-Fi on my laptop gives up." I hoped she did not realize my hidden intention of buying time to enjoy her company somewhat longer. "As I brought only some preparatory notes, but not my map, why don't we use your smartphone again to finalize my itinerary. It could be that I just spend an hour sitting at one of those Blues markers and meditate, try to soak up the atmosphere, get the vibes if you want. We must not lose our connection with the soil and the particular place.

It contains mythical powers that written information cannot reflect, replace or reproduce. Even if buildings are long gone and corpses have decomposed, I expect still to feel an aura." Luther was yawning again and Beth was giving him a look suggesting he cover his mouth.

"Before the aura of helping with the dishes passes, we should get organized." Janice suggested. "Let's get it over with first and do your mapping at the hotel."

"By the way, we have also booked ourselves into the hotel." Luther explained. "Dee—" he saw my perplexed facial expression, "that is Arthur's fireman friend––is waiting for the keys tonight and will take over his temporary care for the house tomorrow morning. I also don't want to sleep again on that forty-year old mattress."

We got up, and with efficient help of all five it did not even take ten minutes to clean up. Luther got Beth's and his own stuff from the bedroom. James deposited the suitcase where he had found it and made sure that Luther locked the regular and security locks on the strengthened entrance door to the harmonica room carefully. Although I had only spent a few hours in the house, I felt sad to leave. Janice helped with some of the window shutters on the first floor. The entrance was locked twice.

I got into my beetle. Beth and Luther had to make a brief detour to see Dee while Janice and James followed me to the hotel. Even if it had been pitch dark and the car without lights, they would still have had a perfect orientation behind me due to the terrible noise my car was now making.

At the hotel, James went straight to his room. Janice and I set next to each other on a two-seater in the lobby, which gave us a perfect excuse to be close without commitment. I double-checked some of the ideas I had jotted down earlier in the year for places to visit in Mississippi, and copied some essential driving instructions from Google maps. Together with my printouts from home in the carry-on it should be sufficient. "Well, let's call it a day." she breathed very close to my face, when I had all the information I needed.

Chapter 8
Cairo - Horn Lake - Oxford

I left Cairo exactly forty-eight hours after my departure from Chicago. The scandalous sound of my beetle was a comforting assurance of continuity, which helped relieve a certain sadness of change and loss. Driving towards the Mississippi bridge, I passed a car dealer's lot full of new and used cars. They surely serviced the wider region. Lot rent must currently be incredibly cheap. I asked myself whether saving on this overhead could produce enough benefit to counterbalance the downsides of the location. Glad not to have to make this and similar business decisions I shifted into fourth gear. This speed produced a gurgle similar to an amplified distortion of a wet draw bend on the first hole of a lower key harmonica. I felt for an A harp in the case lying handy on the front passenger seat. No, it was the B-flat that came closest.

"Good guess!" I slapped myself on the same spot where Janice's arm had lain when she hugged me farewell an hour ago. I was surprised at my sentimentality. Were these still remnants of salty tears that the tip of my tongue tasted on my upper lip? I had all her contact details and she had even indicated she would be happy to host me on my way home from the Delta, should I detour via Dayton, Ohio.

I gave myself another five to seven days for the entire trip. I wanted to bypass Memphis, because it would be too much. Oxford should be first, for two nights. Then into the Delta proper where I might stay in Greenwood for two days. I wondered whether I should go as far south as Jackson, which I had visited ten years ago. The Delta Blues Museum was in Clarksdale, the not-to-be-missed B. B. King Museum in Indianola. That was already plenty on my to-see list. The return trip to Chicago was another two days.

I filled the tank shortly before getting back on I-57 at Charleston, which I then followed south to the intersection with I-55. I planned to stay on the freeway past Memphis and cut across from Batesville to Oxford. While at the outset briefly questioning the wisdom of my driving without constant orientation via sat nav, this felt quite comfortable again. The real world was not replaced by a virtual display of it. I often wondered about the increasing number of pedestrians with headphones plugged in their ears talking apparently to themselves and gesturing wildly. Physically, they were where I saw them, but which world did they live in? Did they notice the ground on which I was walking? If I were a psychotherapist, reawakened after twenty years of artificial coma, I would diagnose them with a major disorder and advise them to seek medical help.

I enjoyed the view through the car windows, got my bearings from the occasional street sign, looked at the speedometer, did a quick calculation of the average speed based on the time spent and miles covered since the last sign. I strained my brain figuring out when approximately the next landmark would come up. Within distances of ten miles, I was anxious not to be off by more than a minute. It keeps you alert when you are driving by yourself. I felt fresh. Two small glasses of wine and a shot of rum atop the banana ice at dinner were not enough to affect me. I had been in bed by ten and slept well past seven this morning. Thinking of my feelings for Janice, I was happy to have refrained from foolish attempts. There was no hangover on that end either.

I listened to various cassette compilations from Chess and Delmark recordings, among them the *Hoodoo Man Blues* with Junior Wells, and to the original cassette of Carey Bell's album *Blues Harp*, which had been an incredible deal for $1.99 at the Delmark store only a month before. Bob Koester, the founder and owner of Delmark, has a firm place in my Olymp of registrars of the African-American songbook.

After 140 miles I looked at my watch. It was just past 11 a.m. Could I really justify skipping Memphis, after spending two nights in Cairo? Egypt as a whole deserved better. I might at least see Beale Street and Handy Park and eat. A stopover of three hours would not jeopardize my planned arrival time in Oxford. Three hours would not be sufficient to do full justice to W. C. Handy, but it would calm my otherwise bad conscience. I did not hesitate long before readjusting my plan for the day.

I would personally inform the natural habitat of Handy that in Germany *handy* had become a household word, being the synonym of *mobile phone*. If he were still alive, would he be merely proud or would he insist that devices carrying his surname must have standard ringtones from *Beale Street Blues* or *St. Louis Blues*? What did Handy think about the dispute in 1941 between Memphis and New Orleans for the premiere screening of the Hollywood movie directed by Victor Schertzinger, *The Birth of the Blues*? Both cities claimed the birthright and each lobbied the film companies in California. The controversy was solved by Paramount's decision to have world premieres simultaneously in both cities.

Did Handy think "Blackface Minstrel Show," when he learned that Bing Crosby played the title role in the production? Being skeptical about Hollywood's seriousness in dealing with the subject, I had watched a few scenes, only to discover that my doubts about the film were justified. The music came close to Jazz, but was certainly not Blues. The creators of the Blues played only a marginal role. I never watched all of it to know whether the harmonica appeared.

"Now, for a change, it would be nice to have a smartphone for checking the options." I thought, sitting in a huge traffic jam on Crump Boulevard, just after exiting the freeway into Memphis. Nothing had moved for twenty minutes. After another twenty minutes of absolute stand still, with the incessant noise of sirens ahead of me, I knew that I had to cancel my plan.

The attempts of revitalizing Beale Street would have to be studied during a separate trip, in combination with a visit of the Memphis Rock & Soul Museum and Graceland. When traffic started moving again, I used the first opportunity for a U-turn to get back on the freeway. In the end I lost almost two hours and was glad to still have a ration of cookies and water from Chicago as a meager lunch substitute.

Crossing the Mississippi state line I remembered Mississippian tourism promotion activities that had caught my attention online and at airports in the planning phase of the Delta tour, and which I, therefore, considered successful. Even without my research interest, I would probably have been intrigued to visit the state and see what remained today of its undeniably violent racial history, so forcefully depicted for example in the movie *Mississippi Burning*. When I had ordered the Blues trail map online, I noticed that the State of Mississippi officially emphasizes that pride in the African-American musical heritage. Obvious signs of the pride are the design of the markers, golden letters on a blue background, and the diligence with which they have been erected across the state. I carried with me the directions to the sites that interested me most, focusing on the *Mississippi saxophone* players, as harpers down there like to call themselves.

Rather than crisscrossing through the state, I wanted to figure out the best order to visit these places and minimize detours between my start and finish lines. Oxford and "Ole Miss" had to be the very first Mississippi destination, because checking out the Blues Archive was key for my research project. Would I also have a chance to meet Adam Gussow whose book *Mister Satan's Apprentice* had made great reading? Horn Lake, birthplace of Big Walter Horton, might still be included, however. Yes, I had an extra half hour for that detour and should still make it to Oxford before 5 p.m.

Figuring this out, with the Blues trail printouts on the front passenger seat, I reached a conclusion and the Goodman Road exit at the same time. From here it was less than a mile to the Horton marker on Center Street. In two minutes I sat in front of my first real Mississippi Blues trail marker. The top of all of them is shaped like a vinyl. In this case it was the depiction of a yellow Sun label record with the title *Easy*. The Sun label had been founded by Sam Phillips in Memphis in early 1950, and other Mississippi sax players like Howlin' Wolf and James Cotton recorded there, before they moved to Chicago. *Easy* was cut in 1953. Despite the clear dominance of the harmonica in the song, the inscription was Jimmy & Walter, following the alphabetical order. Or was it because guitarist Jimmy DeBerry, born in 1911, was Walter Horton's senior? Horton's birthdate is uncertain between 1917 and 1921, probably April 1918. He passed away in 1981.

Of course, *Easy* was in my cassette collection, and sitting in front of the marker, I turned the volume high when it played. The car motor was switched off. With a refreshing breeze coming from the south I wondered, whether Walter's beautiful vibrato was produced gutturally, by a fast back-of-the-tongue movement against the roof of the mouth or by a fluttering hand. I suspected the former, as I had seen a number of YouTube clips with this most awesome vibrator showing no outward motion whatsoever. Looking at his photo, I wondered why he had been called "Big." Was he just standing tall? Had he been a fat little kid? In early English classes in Germany you learned the difference between "big," "tall" and "great." But, apparently "big" among musicians indicated a big name, as can be seen with other harmonica players: Big Bo McGee, Big Daddy Kinsey, Big Jack Johnson, Big Jack Reynolds, Big Leon, Big Mama Thornton, Big George Brock—of whom at least half were not "big" according to any physical scale.

Walter Horton, who had suffered from nystagmus, which gave him the nickname "Shakey," was simply *great*. When he repeated the verse for the third time, he got into the warbles. Did he produce them by moving his mouth along the harp or by moving the harp along the mouth or a combination of both? Again, from the video-clips I knew it was his head moving, hands held steady. Did his disease help him to develop trill control and vibrato as his most outstanding distinctions as a player? Could the harmonica be used in musical therapy?

Nobody was around. Nobody took notice of me except for a German shepherd, barking from a car scrapyard across the street. Was he disturbed by my presence or did he not like my music? I shouted: "Aus, Hasso!" which means: "Cut it off, German shepherd, whatever you may be called!"—one of the rare examples of German being shorter than English. And, to my amazement, the dog fell silent. I fast-forwarded the cassette for a second record whose title *Good Moanin' Blues* was another excellent example of Walter's terrific playing. After locating it on the tape, and returning to my standing position in front of the marker, I noticed in the far corner of my visual field an imposing 300 pound figure who could have been Howlin' Wolf, except that this guy was White. I reversed my opinion that it had been my command that silenced Hasso. There was a far more important authority at the fence with him.

The giant's hands formed a megaphone around his mouth and I understood: ". . . yel . . .pooh?" I knew I was not on Native American territory, where tongues unknown to me were spoken, but in a predominantly White environment, the "greenest city of Mississippi," as Horn Lake's Chamber of Commerce points out. I turned the music low and put a cupped hand behind my right ear.

"Can I help you?" he shouted again.

"Thank you. I'm only studying the Blues marker."

"But what's wrong with your car? I'd be damned if you don't need a new muffler? We heard you comin' down Goodman and turnin' and I thought, 'Finally, the good Lord brought him to me!' I got a '74 sittin' back here with nothin' good any longer 'cept the exhaust system. You can have it for a hundred bucks. A shop around the corner should be able to fix it for under a hundred. C'mon over. I ain't biting like the mosquitoes that will hatch in a couple days, if the weather stays as is."

I stopped the music, took the keys and slammed the door. It made a fast fading clonk-clonk-clonk on the asphalt. I looked under the car. There lay the fucking muffler in all its beauty. I kicked the back tire. "*So'n Scheiß!*" was my outburst in German.

"This must be witchcraft." I thought as I walked over to the guy who was laughing his head off.

"Still!" he told the German shepherd whose neck hair he had grasped in his huge left hand, while he opened the gate with his right.

"I'm Mike." He firmly shook my hand.

"Walter."

"Rex has to see that we are friends." He released the dog, who sniffed my entire lower body up to my belt and whiled a little longer on parts that embarrassed me, before he trotted off. I had never been very afraid of dogs, and simply did not move, with my hands hanging still by my sides.

"Sorry I laughed, but this is just too weird. I can't believe it! Nobody will believe it! You arrive. I make an offer to solve your problem. And, the best is: *You cannot resist*! How long have you been driving with that rotten piece of metal? You better be happy you didn't lose it on the freeway! Where are you from? Most people here prefer country music, by the way."

His talk had given me time to analyze my situation. And, by and by I realized that I was the luckiest son of a bitch on earth. I repented my curse and the kick against the tire. I had been driving from Chicago with a part whose noise level indicated with every additional mile that it needed urgent replacement. I had been putting that off, because I was afraid of having to wait for a replacement due to the age of the car. I stop at my first Blues marker, which happened to be in front of a scrapyard where that exact part was waiting for me. Before, Walter Horton's music had told me first to take it easy and then promised to give me what I now read as "good morning" for the next day. But then—this thought shot through my head—if Mike was mean, he would exploit my situation and raise the price he had demanded *before* the muffler's demise. I was completely in his hands.

Mike had been studying the wrinkles on my forehead. "No worries! I said one hundred and it is one hundred! I'll show you the piece." We walked into a shack with shelves full of car parts. He steered straight to a corner and pulled the stocky VW muffler from a rack. I was unable to detect a storage order system, but he seemed to know exactly where everything was.

From a set of boxes below a wide working table strewn with tools he fetched one that had "Volkswagen 1974" handwritten on the lid. It contained the fixtures.

"Where's the rest of the car?"

"The chassis you mean? It's way back on the grounds, with two more old beetles. But all the usable stuff is in here."

"Cuckoo, cuckoo, cuckoo, cuckoo." made a small mechanical bird from a clock named after it. Mike looked at me: "Yes, I have a *Deutsch* family background. They came from a village in the Black Forest. We'll tow your car to the repair shop. They are still open."

"Credit or debit card?" I asked.

"Neither. Cash only. We'll pass by an ATM."

We walked to his pickup. The entire exhaust pipe system with the fixtures was wrapped in an old blanket. If a member of the National Rifle Association watched us, he might become jealous of the short anti-tank weapon we were carrying about. Rex was guarding the gate as we drove off the yard. Mike parked in front of my beetle, then helped me pull the muffler from underneath it and dump it on his truck. It was no longer hot. He fixed a rope from his tow bar to the beetle's tow eye. I got behind my wheel, shifted in neutral and with the windows open Mike slowly pulled me up Center Street. Fortunately, there was almost no traffic on Goodman and it was not even half a mile to the repair shop. Next to it was a small local bank with an ATM. I faced only two challenges on the short way, to align my steering with the pickup and to be ready to brake. I could have driven that short distance by myself, but this way we avoided emitting carbon monoxide fumes and making noise.

"*Hola, a quién tenemos? Guten Tag, Mike!*" the Mexican (or Guatemalan, or Salvadoran, or Dominican—I never found out and it doesn't make a difference for the immigration discussion) attendant asked.

"*Hola, Eduardo.* My friend here bought a muffler from me and needs it fixed to this yellow beauty. Make him a good price, will you? And, can you do it before tomorrow?"

Hearing them talk I guessed "*Hola*" and "*Guten Tag*" were the only words they knew in Spanish or German respectively. But, surely they were on very good terms with each other.

"*Vamos a ver.*" Eduardo, a worker and Mike pushed the car into the garage and onto the service lift. "Now, show me the new mini hovitzer." Eduardo said. Mike carried it inside while the assistant lifted the car. After examining the old fixtures under the car and looking over the replacement system, Eduardo said to me. "It will cost you 100 bucks tax included, and the car should be ready by nine tomorrow morning."

"That's fine. Thank you."

"*Un placer.*" He stretched out his greasy mechanic's hand, which I gratefully shook.

Mike and I walked over to the ATM. I got 300 dollars and paid Mike. He offered to drive me to a motel 400 yards towards the freeway. I declined and bid him farewell. I wanted to walk. "*Danke*, and regards to Rex!"

"You are welcome. And, don't forget, we prefer country."

I took my baggage out of the car and strolled to the motel. I lost half a day, but got my car repaired, which wasn't bad. The motel had simple, clean rooms with porch chairs facing Goodman. Seven doors to the left I saw one car. If that indicated the level of occupancy, I would not bother anybody with a little harmonica practice. After using the restroom and sorting my stuff I stepped outside. The traffic on Goodman had picked up a little. I had some folksy Joe Filisko/Eric Noden tunes in my head and worked on my breathing and tongue blocking technique.

After an hour or so I became tired and hungry. I dropped the harmonica in my pocket and went across the road to a fast food place. Later I sat in my room at the desk and, for the first time after leaving Chicago, looked at the draft notes I had taken over the course of a few years for my project. Also, the *Chicago Defender* was on my mind as a so-far unexploited resource.

Until eleven that night, the words poured from my head through my fingers into the digital memory hidden behind my laptop's keyboard. The screen began to reveal the story I wanted to tell.

I was awake by seven, did the usual whole body morning routine, packed and had breakfast at the fast food place. Shortly before nine I greeted Eduardo at his shop: "*Buenos días, Eduardo. Como andamos?*"

"*Buenos días. Que bien hablas español! Tu coche está listo.* We checked your oil and tire pressure. You need to top off oil after the next few hundred miles. Other than that the car is in good shape."

They had obviously also washed the car. Eduardo turned the ignition key: A sound like new.

"Beautiful!" I noted and was truly happy.

"It took us a little longer than I thought, but I stick to my promise. It's one hundred bucks total."

"I'm sure your assistant will accept a tip." I passed a twenty-dollar bill over the counter.

"*Gracias*. Have a safe trip."

I had heard of a nice bed & breakfast between the Courthouse Square and the university campus in Oxford, which I wanted to check out. I looked forward to my research in the Blues archive at Ole Miss, curious to see how much work I could get done there in two days.

During the slow one and a half hour drive—the freeway had a lot of traffic—I reviewed the pages I had written the previous night. The Wi-Fi on my laptop worked, the motel had very good internet, and I could easily access the archive of the *Chicago Defender* with my online subscription. Founded in 1905, the publication wanted to raise the social awareness of the Black population and fought for desegregation. As I agreed with Amiri Baraka that Black music and Blues people were intertwined, I wanted to find evidence of Blues related Black consciousness, in particular about the harp and African-American harpers. Discovering that in the 1920s the editor had been Julius Harper, I had great expectations. My disappointment was even greater. Search words based on the instrument and the famous players produced few results. Most of it was already common knowledge like the photo of Stevie Wonder from 1966, holding his chromatic Hohner harmonica into the camera. There were some silly harmonica jokes like the one about the overweight patient whose doctor advises him to play thirty-six holes a day and the patient then goes and buys a harp; curiosities and a few sensational pieces, including the shooting of James Cotton on Oct 2, 1961.

The preference of Jazz over Blues in more sophisticated circles or upper strata of society seemed to reflect also in the music reviews in the *Chicago Defender*. Notable exceptions to largely ignoring the harmonica were a review on April 14, 1928, of "race artist" William McCoy's "novel record," on which he imitates a series of train whistles on the harmonica, and an occasional mention of the large number of harmonica bands in the 1930s. I was convinced the lack of attention to the harmonica had to do with the instrument's overall low reputation. In contrast to its great popularity, it was not before 1948 that Joe Petrillo and his American Federation of Musicians rated the harmonica as a serious instrument and thereby permitted harmonicists as members. There seemed to be a little more coverage of harmonica related events afterwards: a short obituary from May 29, 1954 on harmonica ace Willie Hood "Rhythm Willie," "with his great manipulations of the harp;" a recording session at Chess studios with Howlin' Wolf; reporting on Junior Wells' tour of Europe, including West and East Berlin in 1966. I found also a few anecdotes on how harmonica playing could get one into trouble with the law—obviously Englewood on Chicago's Southside was already heavily gang-infested in 1968—or, on the contrary, help a player to avoid more severe punishment before the judge.

The lack of advertisement in the newspaper was additional evidence that it was not until the second half of the 1960s that Hohner started to pay special attention to African-American players. This was three decades after Rhythm Willie's crowd pleasing live appearances in Chicago and elsewhere in the United States, and more than a decade after Snooky Prior's and Little Walter's first effective use of amplification when playing their Hohner. The unique characteristics of the instrument for musical expression and the genius of African-American players in discovering all its hidden qualities complemented each other accidentally. The relationship existed for at least seven decades without the manufacturer acknowledging it.

The artists were also unaware of this special relationship and did not try to use it to their advantage by approaching the manufacturer with special requests. And, when Hohner finally engaged African American harmonicists like Stevie Wonder, Sonny Boy Williamson II and others as endorsers of its brand in the late 1960s, the Blues had already broken out of the Black neighborhoods and become popular with White people. Hohner, in the same manner that characterized its overall conservative business model for a century, *followed* a safe trend, rather than *set* a trend when it started a new production line in the late 60s with the *Blues harp*.

Chapter 9
Oxford

Arriving at noon at the bed & breakfast, they confirmed a vacancy, but the room was not ready yet. So I left my baggage in the trunk, had a cup of water and walked to the Courthouse Square. Before paying a brief first visit to the Blues Archive, established at the University of Mississippi's Williams Library in 1984, I wanted a quick lunch.

The petals of the magnolia trees were still lying here and there on the lawns, about four weeks after full blossom. Despite my visit occurring past their brief explosion, it was obvious that the abundance of this species in the magnolia state had not been exaggerated in the Mississippi tourism brochures. Their colors contributed to my sensation of this being a White place. Possibly, even the few African-Americans I saw on my stroll to the square and on the square proper had become White at heart and in mind as a result of their academization. Was this the peak of assimilation?

I found a little sandwich place around the corner from the well-known bookstore on the square and had a tuna salad. It was still before the regular check-in time, so why bother to check whether my room was accessible? I had often gotten frustrated and angry about the bureaucratic attitude of innkeepers in this country who denied early access. The public restroom by the square was decent enough to meet my needs. I took my laptop and notes from the car and continued straight to the university campus.

Slightly distracted by squirrels, pigeons and cyclists, I approached the library and startled "This can't be!" The limestone portal, inaugurated in 2006 to commemorate James Meredith's successful application as first African-American in 1962 to be admitted to the segregated University of Mississippi, stood over there all right. But it appeared to me as a gigantic tenth part fragment of a harmonica, consisting of two teeth of the comb with the resonance slot between them. Of course, the reeds were missing, and with a one-hole harmonica even the greatest harp virtuoso in the world would soon be boring his audience. But I loved this allegory: James walking towards the inscription "Courage" above the symbolic entrance to the university, exiting under the inscription "Opportunity," the two other opposite sides of the rectangular monument showing the words "Perseverance" and "Knowledge."

If this indeed were a part of a harmonica, and James had been a harper, the monument would still have an added meaning. Well into the twentieth century it took courage for African-Americans to play the Blues on the harmonica, because they encountered religion-based resistance in their own communities. It was also courageous to play the instrument in the unknown fashion of building a minor scale on the second note of the given key of the harmonica (3rd position) or to play it to a tune whose key was a perfect fourth below the given key of the harmonica (2nd position). The good players would gain opportunities that without the instrument they never had. And, finally, as all musicians know, perseverance in practicing would also give the harper the knowledge and expertise to master his instrument.

The library was just behind the monument. I planned to first look for the relevant harmonica players in advertisement posters related to Blues events, especially from the American Folk and Blues Festival tours through Europe, promoted 1962–70, 1972, 1980–83, and 1985 by the German team Lippmann and Rau. The importance that these festivals had as a source of income for African-American musicians, as an inspiration for European musicians, and as a way of promoting the Blues to European audiences cannot be overestimated. In Germany, it was a common observation—at least in educated circles—that Black-American Blues and Jazz musicians could tour Europe and sleep and eat in hotels and restaurants of their choice, while in their own country they could not even freely choose the cemetery they wanted to be buried at.

Reviewing the posters took two hours. That I found nothing more than what I had already seen in Chicago at the Willie Dixon Blues Heaven Foundation was disappointing.

The remainder of my time was spent scrutinizing the library's catalog and prioritizing the study for the following day. The volume of the material was impressive and could not be exhausted even if I invested an additional week. The filing system permitted a good overview of what was relevant for the harmonica. I was most intrigued with the listing of photographs of harmonica players compiled by the library staff themselves. The seven boxes of the "harmonica project" by Blues archive research associate, Walter Liniger, begun in 1989, and continued by research associate Jonny Miles, looked especially promising. Its focus on communicating with current players about their use of the instrument might lift the veil around the early decades of the harmonica in the United States. Securing the memories and knowledge of still living musicians was essential.

After the library closed, I checked into my room, assessed the splendid porch of the inn and identified my favorite rocking chair for some late evening relaxation. Then I continued to the bookstore on the square. In a comfortable seat in the second floor music literature nook, I got lost in browsing until my stomach indicated that it was time for dinner. *One hundred books every Blues fan should own* by Komara and Johnson had to be put aside reluctantly.

Traveling alone is not nice, unless you are quasi-obsessed with a task that you want to accomplish in a given time. Yet, when eating in places of heavy demand, being single is very often advantageous. So I was extremely lucky to still find a spot on the balcony of one of the restaurants overlooking the square. Getting settled in my chair, I saw Morgan Freeman walking down the street with a lady in his arm. Ah yes, somebody in Chicago had mentioned that he was living in the area. It was almost 8 p.m. and the sun spent his last light for the day. I ordered from the mouth-watering menu and the waitress brought my glass of white wine and water in no time. I anticipated that the food would be exceptionally good, and contribute to my overall contentedness.

Waiting for my food I scanned some material on my laptop, but not yet included in the draft of my research paper. I smiled when I reread a passage from W. C. Handy's autobiography. He mentions a photograph of Joe Louis playing a harmonica with a distorted face after losing his first fight to Max Schmeling by technical knockout in 1936. "Ah hates to see the evenin' sun go down." was purportedly the photo's subline. Joe's revenge would come in the second fight in 1938, when he knocked out Max in the first round. It is not reported whether Joe's harmonica playing helped him prepare for that victory. "A boxer from the country of harmonica players beating a boxer from the country of harmonica makers. This might make a nice punchline somewhere in my final text." I thought.

The outstanding fish entree merited my full attention! After ordering another glass of wine, I went back to my notes on the largely undocumented first decades of the harmonica in the United States and on early Blues. Not even Handy provided much information beyond the assurance that he heard people playing harmonica as early as in the 1880s. Referring to simple song lyrics and melody structures, Handy gives at least an indication of the instrument coexisting with music that might later be called Blues. In contrast, no information whatsoever on the harmonica could be found in *Memphis Music: Before the Blues* by Tim Sharp. What should I make of the fact that, despite substantial German immigration to the area around Memphis, the instrument was not mentioned once? Online research with the Library of Congress had produced a similar void and led me to assume that, in written music and in literature about music, the harmonica was ignored in the United States as a whole until the 1920s. Did all this point again to the underdog status of the instrument? Did its status make it a perfect fit for the underdog African-American player?

Handy's dim light on the coexistence of Black music and the harmonica in the late nineteenth century is somewhat corroborated by Harvard archeologist Charles Peabody, who in a 1903 *Journal of American Folk-Lore* article referred to typical Negro singing as resembling a

"Jew's harp played legato." Checking complex entries on the etymology and usage of "Jew's harp," I concluded that it was never synonymous with "harmonica." Yet, the mystery around the exact origin of the term "Jew's harp" will accompany us for a while longer, just as the byword "French harp" for harmonica can only be unsatisfactorily explained by pointing to its usage in former French territories. The main technical difference is: both have freely swinging reeds, but in the case of the Jew's harp set in motion mechanically, while in the harmonica by the stream of air.

I finished my perusal of notes, closed my laptop and put it in the backpack. I looked over the square with its nightly student life of ethnic diversity not quite reflecting the percentage of the African-American population in the last census. I knew that on Ole Miss campus the percentage of African-Americans was statistically on par with the national average, but the public appearance in front of me was different. The moon above the courthouse shone similarly on innumerous other beautiful locations in the United States whose full appreciation had been denied to the descendants of slaves until fifty years ago. For some strange reason I could not help to think that the harmonica still whined its blue notes to the question where American society really stood on the issue of desegregation in 2015. Beyond the narrower scope of the German harmonica and the American Blues, which I had started off to research, there lay this chunk of history between

President Lincoln's Emancipation Proclamation, Selma and fifty years after. I had to be careful not to choke on it.

The following morning, after breakfast, much tastier than the one from the burger joint in Horn Lake, I headed back to the library. Meredith's dynamic stride gave me the same motivation as the previous day. To my disappointment the video collection held not a single American Folk and Blues Festival video. Bob Shatkin's collection of documents on Blues harmonica history, players and technique in twelve boxes was, however, impressive.

Among many interesting discoveries, the term "devil's toy" for the harp stood out. This meaning had not yet found its way into Google, which listed it as a synonym of skateboard—before entries start drifting off into into the censored adult world. I found this very interesting, as many African-American Blues harpers like DeFord Bailey, Howlin' Wolf, the two Sonny Boys, Blues Birdhead, Big Walter Horton, and Rhythm Willie have told us about the resistance from their parents and neighborhoods who considered the Blues and playing it on the harmonica inappropriate and against the gospel. Given widespread religious aversion to the Blues in its beginnings, I would have expected the term to be more widely used and referenced. It was very sad that Shatkin could not finish his work due to his untimely death in 2001.

The Sheldon Harris collection of sheet music was fascinating in more than one respect. No title page illustration published from around 1900 until the 1940s by white-owned publishing houses showed a harmonica. From today's point of view, the illustrations treated Blues themes in a mostly derogatory manner. Titles that were particularly remarkable in this sense were *Coon, Coon, Coon, Happy little Nigs* and *Eva Dahkey*. Caricatures showed African-Americans dancing, or playing the banjo. They frequently depicted vaudeville scenes with Caucasians in Blackface.

The song *All Coons Look Alike to Me* was popular in 1896. The fact that its composer, Ernest Hogan, was Black himself should not lead us to think that "coon" was non-offensive. It is more likely that Blacks had no other choice than playing along.

Hohner's *Coon Band* harmonica, produced between 1905 and 1924, was widely distributed, including the United States and South Africa, and its allusion to vaudeville motives of the time should be judged against this background. Not only was the Minstrel show a welcome source of income for many actors and musicians, but both Black and White spectators in their segregated sections enjoyed it simultaneously. Before the 1960s this was apparently the only Hohner model that targeted the African-American consumer.

Increasing noise around me became a nuisance. Yet, before beginning to complain, I looked at the clock. I had apparently gotten lost in incessantly checking off my to-do list since entering the library in the morning. It was 4:50 p.m. The library was about to close, and it was a Friday, the last working day for the week. I had managed to get an overview of the archive's complex material, and gained enough confidence to say that, even in these specialized archives, information on the first fifty years of the harmonica in the United States was limited. So, packing up, I was not frustrated. The loop through Mississippi in the next few days would provide insights on a different scale.

Having skipped lunch I decided to have an early dinner in a cafeteria on campus. The tables were occupied with typical representatives of the internet generation, for whom the computer was as essential as had been book, notepad and pen during my student years. Realization that the web contained true and false information and was an excellent platform for manipulation was masked by the convenience. Personal communication had been largely replaced by virtual communication. I was out of danger. Not only, because age helps to develop a sound critical distance, but because my laptop's internet connectivity was no longer working.

I stopped to buy a six-pack of beer on the way back to my bed & breakfast.

"Good evening, Sir." somebody on the porch said as I arrived. His strong accent and the formal greeting indicated that he was a foreign tourist, most likely from a

German speaking country, who wanted to prove on the one hand he did not belong to the reserved northern Europeans, on the other hand he did not like—or did not know —how informal Americans meet and introduce themselves. He was in his early 50s.

"Hi," I said, "did you just arrive? Where are you from?"

"I am from Frankfurt." he replied.

"*Also sind Sie Deutscher?*" I continued to ask.

He seemed embarrassed, as we Germans always are when we meet other German tourists.

So I immediately added: "I have lived in this country for over fifty years. If you want to practice your English that's fine with me."

"*Danke sehr.* That would be good for me. I was never in America. Some of my ancestors settled in Germantown, Memphis, in the 1850s. They landed in New Orleans and then with steamboat up the Mississippi." He was now more relaxed, spoke slowly, but accurately in his rusty school English.

"Can I join you? Would you like a beer? It's still cold. I just bought it."

"*Danke, sehr gerne. Ich bin übrigens Herr Schäfers.*" He held out his hand.

"*Guten Abend, Herr Schäfers*. I'm Walter." I said shaking his hand.

"I arrived in New Orleans before four days." (I did not correct him.)

"*Prost*." I said.

"*Prost*. Tomorrow I go to Memphis and in two other days fly back."

"Nice trip. What have you seen so far?"

"In New Orleans I was in the French Quarter. After the hurricane everything is good again. I listened to Jazz and ate Creole food. I love it, how do you say: '*scharf gewürzt*'?"

"Spicy or hot. I can't eat spicy. So you spent two days in New Orleans?"

"Yes, then I drove to Jackson."

"Did you like it? I have some good memories of a bar near the old capitol building."

"Yes, I liked it. The capitol is full of history. The area around my hotel downtown was not very nice, but still okay. And I went hiking at the Barnett Reservoir."

"So you are mostly interested in visiting the region to which your ancestors emigrated?"

"I am also interested in young American history.

Today I passed through Philadelphia."

"You must be kidding."

"What is 'kidding'?"

"Make a joke. In German *'jemanden auf die Schippe nehmen'*."

"No. I wanted to see the place where James Chaney, Andrew Goodman and Michael Schwerner were killed."

"Those guys mean something to you? Amazing! You know, what my plans were for tonight? I wanted to get the DVD *Mississippi Burning* and watch it in my room, because the Wi-Fi on my laptop is down. I arrived in Chicago in 1962, two years before the events of June 21, 1964, when the Klan members and law enforcement officers colluded in the murders. Gene Hackman is one of my favorite actors."

"I saw it only once after its—when it came out— in 1989. My Wi-Fi works. We can watch it together out here? That is more fun."

"Great idea. When? I have already eaten. You probably haven't had dinner yet."

"I bought a sandwich in a supermarket. Let me get my computer."

After his return and while he was searching for a

streaming service, he talked about Neshoba County and Philadelphia in particular: "I went into the local tourist office. The lady said: 'We have changed.' She was very happy that I visited despite the ugly history of the town. I felt very welcome in two other shops, but am still thinking about what one shopkeeper said, when I asked him how life was like: 'You are a visitor. I live here.' I went to the Black township, Carver, to see the old office of the Center of Federated Organizations from the '60s, where activists met. A guy near a *'Andenkengeschäft?'*—" "Curio or memorabilia shop," I offered. "Yes, from this curio shop, said: 'It is much better now. We got a Black mayor in his second term.' People seem still traumatized. At the killing place, some miles out of town, the marker states that the three activists had gone there to investigate the burning of Mt. Zion Church. Do you believe that this crime helped the passage of the Civil Rights laws?"

"Yes, I do. Another example that often something terrible must happen first before an intolerable situation can begin to improve."

He had found a streaming service and we watched the film.

"*Herr Schäfers*, don't you think it's still power-ful?"

"*Ja,* Walter. My first name is Werner."

Our well had long run dry and it was past nine

o'clock.

"I spent the whole day in the library and I'm tired." I said. "Tomorrow morning I'm off to Greenwood in the Delta." He inquired about my interest there and I gave him the shortest possible version in German to make it easier. He let me go after thirty minutes.

"*Gute Nacht*!"

"See you in the morning. Night."

Chapter 10
Oxford - Greenwood

We briefly bumped into each other on the stairs leading from the rooms to the first floor. Werner had already had breakfast. With "*Gute Reise!*" our paths parted for good. Being a little late I regretted not having enough time for a visit of the Faulkner Mansion in Rowan Oak. But, on the other hand, Faulkner's work was too distant from my topic.

I put on the Alligator records cassette *In My Time* from 1993 with Charlie Musselwhite, who had recently become an endorser of Seydel harmonicas. The boogie groove of *Leaving Blues* coincided with passing the Oxford exit sign. For less than an hour, to the music from the album, including some repeats, I followed Highway 7 south along the Holly Springs National Forest all the way to 51, which took me straight into Grenada.

The Grenada Blues marker at the corner of First and Main Streets is crowned by a Bluebird label vinyl replica of *Come Back, Baby* by Blues pianist Walter Davis. It informs about several other musicians from the area, among them the singer-harmonica player Big George Brock, who I had come for in the first place. He belongs to the large stock of solid, but lesser known Blues singers and harpers. I had read about him also in Roger Stolle's book *Hidden History of Mississippi Blues*, which otherwise contains only little information on harpers and their instrument, despite its cover showing a harmonica case. Born 1932 on a plantation in Yalobusha County, outside of Grenada, Brock lived and worked for some time with Muddy Waters near Clarksdale. His way of holding and playing the harmonica with the low register in the right hand corner of his mouth is rare. He is promoting St. Louis as the seat of a National Blues Museum, believes in the healing power of the Blues and insists that Blues musicians should above all be authentic. In a 2013 interview he complained that the real Blues was disappearing everywhere and had been doing so for fifteen years.

The marker displays a photo of Brock, possibly in his late twenties, and a vinyl cover of one of Brock's recent records produced on Roger Stolle's record label Cat Head. In another photo he holds a harmonica with his right hand into the camera—one of the typical portrait poses of harpers. Another harmonica player from the area who migrated to Chicago was Alford 'Blues King' Harris (1925-1986). Together with Walter Horton he appears on a critically acclaimed Delmark album of '50s style Blues

Harmonica Blues Kings.

I realized that I was probably just an hour away from Musselwhite's birthplace with the good Polish name Kosciusko. Charles is not African-American, but proud to have Native American blood from his mother's side. Kosciusko lay almost halfway between Grenada and Philadelphia to the southeast. Grenada and Greenwood, my next destination, would be the closest I got to the real scene of last night's movie action. Werner's remarks about the apparent traumatization of the population rang in my ears. I felt like "Mississippi Learning."

Finally entering the territory called Mississippi Delta, which is not the mouth of the Mississippi but lies way north, roughly between Memphis and Vicksburg, my impressions of the land changed continuously depending on the angle of the sun. I had to be taught by locals that what I saw as hopeless huge dusty plains in shades of brown, even grey to anthracite, were indeed the richest soils in the United States. I just happened to pass between harvesting time and the first signs of growth of new cotton plants as the ground was recovering and gathering strength for a new productive cycle. The irrigation systems spanned the entire width of the fields of half a mile or longer. I had never seen anything like it.

I entered the parking lot of a hotel in Greenwood. Like many other small American towns, despite heavy investment in restoration and maintenance, the center seemed like an open-air museum without people. The mall on the outskirts had taken away downtown business––a phenomenon more and more common in Germany also. The hotel had a vacancy and—oh wonder!—I could move in immediately, although it was only 11 a.m. The African-American receptionist cautioned me not to stray into the side streets too far at night.

What would I want to see there anyhow? A similar warning came from the White owner of an art gallery around the corner. These cautionary remarks accompanied me, while I continued to follow for two more days, in a non-discriminatory way, the directions of the Blues trail map.

I started to tour the eight Blues markers in and around Greenwood. Although none of them is particularly harmonica related, there is the towering figure for the Blues in general of singer-guitarist Robert Johnson. Many mysterious stories are woven around his short life and death in 1938, by poisoning at twenty-seven. A vinyl replica of his *Cross Road Blues* appropriately tops the marker at his gravesite. In 1968, the song was unconsciously my first acquaintance with this composer, when the British band Cream, with Eric Clapton on guitar, released its version *Crossroads*. The gravesite lies to the north of Greenwood in a bend where Money Road meets the Tallahatchie River.

Only a few miles further north in Money is the

grocery store, where, in the summer of 1955, fourteen-year-old Chicago South Side kid, Emmett Till, had an encounter with Carolyn Bryant, a White woman behind the counter. She complained to her husband about how Emmett had looked at her. Some hours later, Bryant's husband and his half-brother fetched the boy from the great-uncle whom he was visiting for the summer, brutally beat him, shot him dead and dumped him in the Tallahatchie. The killers were acquitted by a White jury, and later publicly admitted that they had committed the crime.

One gets to Johnson's gravesite and the grocery store, by crossing the bridge made famous by country girl and singer, Bobbie Gentry, born 1944. She went to school in Greenwood and her song *Ode to Billy Joe*, released in 1967, became a big hit, also in Europe. Visiting in a little more than an hour the Blues marker for Robert, the Civil Rights trail marker for Emmett and the red Mississippi country music trail marker for Bobbie had a powerful impact on me. It added a new dimension to my musical memories. The musicians' backgrounds were similarly rural and poor. But, after childhood, segregation forced them into their parallel worlds. The three sites, only a few miles apart on the edges of huge cotton fields, illustrated quite well the historical, social and political complexities that lie behind the Mississippi Blues.

Robert Johnson had last lived in the Baptist Town part of Greenwood, according to Blues singer-guitarist, David "Honeyboy" Edwards, who passed away aged ninety-five in 2011. That was where I headed next. The marker there idealizes the district's former close-knit neighborhood. Sonny Boy Williamson II allegedly played frequent gigs with Johnson and Edwards at the nearby Three Forks juke joint. I did not see anybody, when I stopped at the McKinney Chapel M. B. Church, and could not ask whether the neighborhood fabric still existed. The area looked poor. Maybe it was one of those that the hotel receptionist would have included in her warning.

Past the eastern end of Baptist Town, in front of *WGLN* radio station, stands the "Blues Deejays" marker. It highlights the role of radio disc jockeys since the 1940s, and their early conflicts with the American Federation of Musicians and the American Society of Composers, Authors and Publishers. AFM and AASCAP were vehemently opposed to substituting live music by records. They tried their utmost, but finally in vain, to prevent the distribution of prerecorded music over the airwaves. Furthermore, the marker informs about African-American owner-operators of radio stations, of course, not missing Ruben Hughes who purchased *WGLN* in 1988. This marker plus the *WGRM* radio station marker in downtown Greenwood, where B. B. King had his first radio appearance in a gospel ensemble, provided a lot of general information on the relationship between radio and Blues artists. B. B. King is probably the most famous Blues musician whose career start was helped by a contract with a radio station, when he promoted the elixir Pepticon at *WDIA* in Memphis. Sonny Boy Williamson II is probably the most famous harper who got a career boost by radio. He had a contract with *KFFA* in Helena, Arkansas, to promote King Biscuit flour, and gave B. B. the opportunity to make his first radio experience. Both musicians initially profited more from the opportunity to perform live on the air than from the play of their records.

The stories told by the markers and my impressions at the sites gave me plenty to brood about. Before returning to my room I strolled up and down Howard Street. A decent bookshop was open. An in-house winery with Mississippi wine offered a welcome opportunity to learn about other aspects of Mississippian life, and relax a little during a tasting. An early dinner at a relatively new restaurant, was not bad, but did not reach the quality level of the first dinner in Oxford. Hardly anybody was in the streets, but there were customers inside all the shops.

At the hotel, a large festively dressed African-American party had begun to celebrate a wedding, and the first people were already moving to the sounds of a band playing soul and funk music in the ballroom. The rhythms penetrated walls and ceilings up to my room on the third floor where I had resumed my writing.

Chapter 11
Berclair - Moorhead - Dunleith
- Leland - Indianola

The next morning, Riley B. B. King's birthplace was my first stop. I somehow missed Highway 82 exit for Itta Bena recommended by my Blues Trail map and had to drive back a few miles. A road that soon changed to gravel took me to a patch at the intersection of 513 and 305 Leflore County roads that featured a withered tree, possibly struck by lightning years ago, and was bordered by a small forest at the edge of Bear Creek.

The marker showed a photo of the Berclair train station from the 1920s, with a separate entrance for "colored." I recalled a video documentary in which B. B. King, during a bus travel to this site, explained his humble beginnings. The drops of the drizzling rain on the swamp-like surface waters reminded me of the tears in the 1960s. Segregation was still normal in the South at the time of my arrival in the United States. Roughly a decade later, the U.S. administration would be at the forefront of global sanctions against the apartheid regime in South Africa.

One hundred yards behind the marker, I found tombstones of an apparently informal cemetery with the last grave from the year 2000. Opposite were open cotton fields stretching one or two miles to a line of more trees on the horizon. A low farm building with a few silos lay just across from the site.

The location of the sharecropper's cabin that had been King's home until 1929, the first four years of his life, was half a mile away, but no longer standing. He spent the rest of his childhood with his grandmother in Kilmichael. At eighteen, he got a job as tractor driver in Indianola and since then he called that town his home. My visit to his museum there would be the final stop for the day.

I went on to Moorhead. Although no known harper comes from there, I thought that the place, like a few others in the Delta, exemplified the musicians' need for transportation to their gigs. The Moorhead marker communicates well the importance of the railroad in what was still a frontier location in 1890. There the Yazoo Delta Railroad crosses the Southern Railway. Handy got the inspiration for his title *Yellow Dog Blues* in Tutwiler 1903 where he first heard the song *Goin' Where the Southern Cross the Dog*. The place also symbolizes the great inspirational power that different train noises and their whistles had for sound imitation on the harmonica. Think of William McCoy, DeFord Bailey and generations of later players. Most students of the harp today try to learn at least the basics of producing such sounds, even if they lack experience with real steam locomotives.

I put on a demo cassette of Joe Filisko, one of the great harmonica instructors in the Chicago area. Following with high concentration his train imitation lesson I was breathing, puffing and hissing along for a while on my C harp until I noticed that a couple of young African-American kids had gathered around me. Their bewildered eyes offered just two interpretations: I was doing a very bad job or they could no longer relate to the story. Asked whether they knew the name of my instrument, only one of the ten answered timidly: "Mississippi saxophone?" "Right on!" I said. "You earned yourself a reward." But, none of them understood my question about the railroad tracks in the ground that had been left to give further credibility to the textual information of the marker. I was happy that the quality of my practice had not been the reason for their strange looks and bought all of them some candy at a shop run by an Indian gentleman across the street.

I took a short northern detour to Dunleith from Highway 82 for the marker in honor of Mathis James "Jimmy" Reed (1925-1976), with a replica of his successful VeeJay Record *You Don't Have To Go* from 1954. Epilepsy did not prevent him from being a good musician, but heavy drinking was not conducive to a long life expectancy. Two photos from performances in the '60s show him with his harmonica neck rack and an electric guitar.

Combining singing with two instruments was a big exception among African-American players, which may explain the inscription that ranks him as "one of the most influential Blues artists of the 1950s and '60s," and emphasizes his acceptance, both by Rhythm & Blues and by pop music listeners.

I felt attracted to Reed, having in younger days offered the same musical "package deal" that he maintained, until the end of his career. As bands like the Rolling Stones covered some of his songs, he can be considered a successful songwriter. A better harper was, in my opinion, Willie Foster (1921-2001) to whom the marker refers as a childhood friend of Reed's, adding that he bought his first harmonica at age seven for twenty-five cents from self earned money.

My next stop was Leland. Blues guitarist Johnny Winter (1944 - 2014), who became a star in the '60s, had spent part of his childhood there as well as Willie Foster who came from here. My friend Robie had all of Winter's vinyls in his collection. I had only one. Both of us were somehow fascinated by his albinism and the fact that, as a child of upper-class Whites, he had made the Blues his favorite form of artistic expression. Not to forget that he played with harmonica greats like Walter Horton and, in the '60s, was well established in the Chicago scene.

Now I was ready to return to Indianola for my extensive visit to the B. B. King Museum. It is not listed on the Blues Trail map and I was wondering why this was the case, as I followed the signs to it from U.S. 82. The exhibits turned out to be irrelevant for my special harmonica interest, but they helped answer some questions and reconfirm some views that were important for my work.

For example I read about B. B.'s determination to give all of his children a good education. Recalling my conversation with Janice and James, and given the enormous costs of education in the States, I considered that to be a valid explanation and noble excuse for being short of money and having to tour until old age.

I saw a statement by B. B. expressing surprise that, a White audience welcomed him and gave him a standing ovation at his San Francisco concert in 1967. This confirmed my observation about the audience of the Blues changing in the '60s from Black to White. I also took note of the comment under the sign "Schreibstube," of a German prisoners of war camp in Indianola, pointing out that World War II prisoners in that camp were sometimes treated better than African-Americans.

Overall I liked the didactic concept of the museum, especially its emphasis on the interconnectedness between the Blues and the Civil Rights movement. Some panels explain in a sober way that B. B. felt limitations to supporting the movement with political statements. They claim that he preferred to give behind-the-scenes financial grants to activists and their families. However, concrete evidence of this is meager. Does the poster of a "homecoming" concert that B. B. gave as late as 1989 for Medgar Evers, the Civil Rights activist gunned down in 1963 in Jackson, prove the claim? Are there no better examples?

I jotted down another critical observation: The true scope of the European enthusiasm for the Blues since the 1960s is not fully acknowledged. It stretched far beyond the United Kingdom. Nevertheless I decided to rank the museum as highly recommendable in the manuscript I was drafting.

Back in the hotel, my head was spinning, not from a wealth of information, but from a lack of food. I enjoyed dinner in a typical family restaurant, recommended by trip advisor. During the meal I overheard a conversation at the neighboring table.

". . . I don't think it was bad at all, don't you agree?"

"You don't have to be a gambler to be staying in a casino hotel. They really can't afford to be bad or overpriced."

"Tunica still has problems, but I think they stopped the population drain with the build-up of the gambling industry. I'm only surprised this tradition has survived along the Mississippi . . ."

These cue words were enough to give me an idea for the following night. I asked the hotel receptionist whether she had any information about Tunica. It so happened that she was originally from Helena, Arkansas, and her current boyfriend was working in one of the Tunica casinos. My run of luck on this journey from Luther, Janice, James and the harmonica collection, the muffler repair, to great discoveries about the Blues continued. I could barely restrain myself from jumping over the counter and hugging the girl. At the last moment I realized the risks of breaking a leg in the attempt or of being charged with sexual harassment.

Back in my room I compared the information gathered so far on my thesis about the mutually beneficial relationship of the harmonica and the Blues. Looking at my notes I realized that the story was pretty much told. More markers would not necessarily add to the essence. I could now be even more selective. I would finish my excursion into the Blues the next day, stay in Tunica and then drive back to Chicago in two days.

My habit of regularly pushing the "save" button prevented a major disaster that night.

Writing in the armchair, which was more comfortable than the desk chair, I nodded off and found myself about fifteen minutes later with my hands in an odd position on the keyboard. The screen had not gone blank. Instead, there were endless lines of question marks. I scrolled back for a minute deleting them till I reached the text, which was still there. Sadly the world's problems cannot be handled like this!

I needed some exercise to get over my sleepiness. Why not organize the contents of my jumbled suitcase? I walked over to the rack on which it lay open. There were far too many clothes. The only excuse was the vanity of age and the uncertainty of the duration of the trip. Yet, vanity had taken a backseat since day two of my tour.

Suddenly, through layers of clothes, from the bottom of my suitcase, a book cover called. You have yet to read me! I had absolutely forgotten about the copy of *BluesSpeak* by Lincoln T. Beauchamp, Jr. (Chicago Beau), which I had bought a month ago. Of key interest was the interview Beau did with Junior Wells in 1992.

After I was satisfied with my how-to-get-fit-in-five-minutes-without-sweating practice by reorganizing the suitcase content, I lay down on the bed and read the book.

Beau's interview with Junior opened my eyes to an aspect of the relationship between the harp and the American Blues that I had not thought of before. As official American "Blues Ambassador," on tour in the service of the U.S. Department of State, Junior Wells blew and sucked on the German harp all around the world. I now fully grasped the meaning of the inscription on his tombstone "Bluesman to the world."

Junior tells about his tours to Africa in 1967 or '68, and that he was with Vice President Hubert Humphrey in the Ivory Coast. Humphrey commended him for doing more with his concerts in a few days than U.S. diplomacy had achieved in thirty years. In appreciation, he arranged for Junior, who was already in his mid-thirties, to finish high school. Junior declined to do the tour of South Africa to which he was invited next, because he refused to stay in a hotel where South African Blacks had no access.

Some of the interview passages on the situation in the United States sound quite frustrated, especially when Junior talks about Blacks killing each other and not getting anything else right except for that. He is just as critical about their lack of cultural identification and their materialistic attitude. As to how he got to play harmonica, there was the most comprehensive story I had seen. After moving up to Chicago with his mother in 1941 at age seven, he was first only "messing around with the harmonica." During a visit to his former home near Memphis, he met Sonny Boy Williamson II and asked him to teach him to play.

The next part of the interview is so interesting that it needs to be quoted verbatim:

"So he said 'Let me see your harp.' And I had one of them old American Ace harps. And he throwed it to the ground and stomped on it. He said 'Don't never bring no mess like that in front of me. If you want a harmonica, you buy a harmonica, you know. You buy you a harp. Don't come in here with that mess.' Harps wasn't but about 15 cents at the drugstore, you know. They had a Rexall drugstore up there on the highway; and I went there and got me one."

Unfortunately, the question, which make and model Junior's teacher was playing then, remains unanswered. One can only say that he obviously appreciated quality. A precise date of the incident would be necessary to take a guess. Junior's seventh birthday in 1941 coincided with the year of the United States entry into World War II, after which regular shipments of German harmonicas— through legal channels at least—ended for some time. The account of Mathew Hohner in New York was blocked in the fall of 1941. During the war, the Hohner factory was forced by the armament ministry of the Third Reich to produce detonators, and could only use drastically rationed raw material for a limited production of instruments solely for the domestic market.

I woke up with the book on my belly. The sun was shining. It was six thirty. I took a shower, changed, packed up my books, had a cappuccino and a muffin in the restaurant and checked out.

Chapter 12
Glendora - Tutwiler - Lambert
- Clarksdale - Helena - Tunica

From Greenwood I took U.S. 49 to Glendora, where a poster welcomed me to the birthplace of the "King of the Harmonica," Sonny Boy Williamson II. One of the two official Mississippi Blues trail markers for Junior Wells' harp teacher has been erected here. It is crowned with the replica of a Checker vinyl *Don't Start Me Talking*. His birthdate is uncertain, but the family decided to put "Mar 11, 1908" on the tombstone in Tutwiler. This makes him six years older than the harper whose alias he adopted, and who was killed in Chicago as early as 1948.

Sonny Boy was a prolific songwriter, convincing singer and influential harmonica player. His international tours took him far away from the sixteen-mile line between Glendora and Tutwiler and let him gather global fame. The anecdote Junior Wells told about his treatment by him might lead us to think that he was a bad teacher. If showing the licks and explaining to a student the technical tricks is the measure, then skepticism seems justified. If you measure by success, as Junior concedes later in the same interview, then Sonny's roughness was the decisive provocation for Junior to prove he could do it. With successful titles like *Eyesight to the Blind*, *Help Me*, *Your Funeral and My Trial*, *Fattening Frogs for Snakes*, *Nine Below Zero*, and many, many more on Trumpet Records (1951-1954) and Chess (1957-1964), it was no wonder that Hohner was eager to sign a contract with him as an endorser of its Marine Band model.

The marker inscription does not ignore a negative aspect of Sonny's, calling him a "trickster who was often in trouble with the law." It excuses harsh character traits with possible physical abuse which he may have suffered, pointing out that in 1915 the Governor of Mississippi reprimanded the owner of the plantation where Sonny was born for mistreatment of African-Americans. Tallahatchie County was infamous for many lynchings.

In Tutwiler, a locomotive sculpture, with the inscription "1905" and "Tutwiler" greeted me. Capital letters below it claim: "WHERE THE BLUES WAS BORN." I found an unofficial makeshift Blues marker in the village center—very sympathetic, with the barely decipherable inscription: ". . . the final resting place of 'Sonny Boy' Williamson." Next to it, the official Blues marker memorializes Handy with his *Yellow Dog Blues* inspiration at this train station in 1903. Tutwiler might want to correct the date at its welcome sculpture, I noted.

I continued to Lambert in Quitman County, where James "Snooky" Pryor (1921-2006) was born. After listening carefully to *Snooky's & Moody's Boogie*, recorded together with Moody Jones in 1948 by the ominous Planet record label, I had come to the conclusion that the theme of *Juke* that catapulted Little Walter to fame four years later, in 1952, successfully copied the original with a better groove. Although deserving additional recognition as one of the pioneers of the post-World War II Chicago Blues electric sound, and for being probably the first to cup the harmonica with a microphone in his hands, Pryor does not have his own marker. He is, however, mentioned under "Sunnyland Slim" and "Mississippi to Maine" in the marker list, which pop up if you enter Pryor or Snooky in the search field.

The marker mentions a one-armed harper Big John Wrencher (1923-1977), who had roots in Quitman County and became a fixture on Maxwell Street market in Chicago in the 60s. Provine "Little" Hatch Jr. (1921-2003) from Sledge, Quitman County, is the third harper listed. He is most likely the only African-American harmonica player "discovered" by German exchange students. This happened in Kansas City in 1970, when they recorded two of his performances in a club under field conditions. A rare pressing, distributed by the German M & M label in 1974, was offered online in 2011 for around fifty dollars.

Entering Clarksdale from the south, I passed the sculpture of three blue semi-acoustic guitars and the highway signs 49 and 61, titled "The Crossroads." My main destination was the Delta Blues Museum. Since the late '80s the Sunflower River Blues Festivals have taken place next door. I spent almost two hours there, most of that time in front of three separate display cabinets for Sugar Blue, Charlie Musselwhite and Sonny Boy Williamson II. The number of harmonicas, all of them by Hohner, attested to the high reputation of the make among these top players. The structural remains of Muddy Waters' cabin have been relocated to the museum and seemed to be the main attraction for the more generally interested visitor.

Other places of interest for Blues aficionados in Clarksdale are the Rock & Blues Museum of Theo Dasbach, a retired Dutch banker, and Roger Stolle's shop. Theo has a number of autographed Hohner harmonicas on display.

Before continuing to Helena, I briefly stopped at some other markers in Clarksdale and environs, if only to make sure I didn't overlook anything. At the old Riverside Hotel, where Black musicians used to stay, the death in 1937 of Bessie Smith after a car accident on Highway 61 just outside of town is the main theme. The marker in the "New World" part of town calls this area "a breeding ground of ragtime, Blues, and jazz music" at the end of the nineteenth century, and honors Handy who lived in Clarksdale from 1903 to 1905. For soul music star, Sam Cooke (1931-1964), who spent the first two years of his life here before his parents moved to Chicago, a separate marker is duly reserved. *A change is gonna come* was released in 1964, at the peak of political and social expectations. When I saw the dead tree at Stovell Plantation, Muddy Waters' birthplace, I thought of the tree stump at the B. B. King marker. Two monuments of fallen giants.

A brief detour took me to the second official Sonny Boy Williamson II marker of the day in Helena, Arkansas. It was only dedicated in 2014 and recalls the Checker hit *Bring it on Home* from 1965, with a photo of Sonny playing the harp swallowed lengthwise in his mouth, just as he sometimes played through mouth and nose in parallel. To me that had always been artistry aimed more at a circus audience than at the connoisseur of the Blues.

I arrived in Tunica at about 5 p.m. During the day I became aware that the highways I was using were probably the most important arteries of the Delta Blues bloodstream. Going by the number of songs composed about it, U.S. 61 far surpasses U.S. 49. But, simply by recapping the references of players along the stretch from Glendora to Clarksdale, I felt U.S. 49 could compete well.

The last destination of the day was the marker of James Cotton, born in 1935, with the Sun Record title *Cotton Crop Blues*. At age five or six he began to imitate trains and hens on the harp, but was one of the players who had to cope with the resistance of their parents to playing the Blues. Luckily, James did not allow himself to be discouraged. His friendship with Paul Butterfield and Mike Bloomfield enabled him to cross over into rock and find new audiences and explore new territories for the harmonica. On the way from the Cotton marker to the casino hotel on the outskirts of town I tried to play along with the interpretation by his sidemen of *It was a very good year*.

The check-in was quick. The way from the reception to my room led me past the one-armed bandits, in front of which people sat spending their coins hoping to gain coins. This provoked a strange sensation relating to the one-armed octogenarian singer in Jackson a decade ago, and to Big John Wrench. In my imagination their beautiful music grew louder and quickly drowned the profane sound of gambling.

I was having dinner, when the friend of the Greenwood hotel receptionist introduced himself. She had informed him that I might drop in, and he had been on the alert. He was extremely friendly and appreciative. Whether everything was to my satisfaction, he asked. When I confirmed, he wanted to know, if I still planned to drive to Chicago in the next two days. I confirmed. He inquired whether it had to be two days or could also be faster. I confirmed, but added that I could no longer drive so many hours in a day. Well, he said, if that was a problem, he had the answer. "What is it?" I asked.

"My friend has to get to Chicago by tomorrow

night."

"You mean your friend from Greenwood?"

"No, the assistant of this hotel's manager."

"Aah," I said.

"Would it be okay, if he drove you?"

It was a very good year was ringing in my ears again. "Yes, of course." I replied. "Let's leave at eight."

"Fantastic."

It took a while until my euphoria calmed down. I would be back a day early and not have to overnight again on the road. Perfect. I finished my meal and retired to my room.

Chapter 13
Back in Chicago and getting ready for Germany

His name was Bill. I drove the first three hours until 120 miles north of Memphis on I-57. We took a short break for the usual, got gas and he took over. We filled the tank once again halfway between the first stop and Chicago, had some food from the lunch bag his friend had generously provided, and Bill drove tirelessly until we arrived at my house at about 6 p.m. I thanked him and he got a cab at the corner.

Despite not having held the steering wheel myself for the last six hours I was dead tired, but very happy. It had been impossible to see all of the exciting places in Mississippi and along the way during one single trip. But my choice had provided a good sample and the insight was deep. The complexities of the American South remained. I had listened to great music on the way and my muffler was repaired cheaper than I could have had it done in Chicago. So I believed at least, until I leafed through the automotive section of the Sunday paper and found an ad: "Complete muffler replacement for '70s beetles and super beetle for $ 159.99, labor incl."

I had made some new friends. One lived in the neighborhood. His cousin in Dayton and her son were particularly close now. I had been spared Schultze's fate and I felt fitter than before, despite clocking 1,600 miles. My mailbox was full with all sorts of the usual junk. A friend living in Germany had told me that it was customary there to put stickers on your mailbox indicating you did not want advertisement. None of the people I knew in Chicago had ever heard of this option. While sorting out the inevitable bills and few private letters that came still by surface mail, I was excited to find a handwritten letter from James sent just two days before, four days after we had bid farewell. I opened it immediately.

"Dear Walter,

"I trust this letter finds you well after returning from your musicological, sociological and historical journey. You implanted a bug in me. It has been keeping me awake for two nights in a row and I fear it will only come to rest after you respond in writing, by email or telephone; see my cell number above. (I hope it comes handy! Giggle.) If I am lucky you will be home by Tuesday."

This was Tuesday!

"On the return trip with mother—who likes you

very much, by the way—we discussed Arthur's bequest. Mother and Luther are determined to sell the house, as they are not interested in moving to Cairo. They are also afraid that tenants might give them more constant headache than regular financial income. They approached their neighbor Dee.

"Apparently he is seriously considering buying the house. He has no intention to leave the area and wants to take some of his larger family in to fill up the space. It seems like he is already thinking of his old age and wants to secure some future help. Both, mother and Luther are willing to accept an offer that has what I would call a 'serious charity discount.' The advantage of a fast transaction is the immediate security of the house. The buyer's temporary caretaking has already been modified to him moving in full time. No, not quite fully. He is accepting our condition to keep the harmonica salon locked up and untouched for at least one year beyond the date of sale. This makes the continued insurance of the collection at an estimated value of 20,000 dollars easy. It also saves me the expenses of transporting and storing it somewhere else.

"Concerning my own attitude towards the bequest, unless I am forced by circumstances not under my control," ("Such as falling in love with a woman who cannot stand harmonicas," I thought.) "I have decided to keep the collection at all costs and proudly preserve this heritage. I went through all the stuff in the suitcase. Although I am not a historian and can't read German, as you noticed, your initial comments on the content, and some further investigation I undertook, have convinced me of the collection's value. I am actually intrigued to look at job opportunities in instrument production, marketing and distribution. Janice encouraged me when I mentioned the idea to her. I know that this is not a field where one makes a fast buck—if one is fortunate enough to get into one of the rare vacancies in the first place. But, it looks more intellectually fulfilling than other options in automotive or food branding I had thought of before, especially given my new situation.

"In one of our conversations you mentioned the huge amount of information accessible on the web. I have started to check whether I could verify some of your critical remarks about the apparent lack of serious involvement of my people with our history. I must say you are right. Aside from a few autobiographies, there is clearly more scientific or popular writing about the Blues and the harmonica by Whites than by African-Americans.

"Also, if you look at online harmonica instruction, there is barely one African-American instructor, although my ancestors were undeniably the ones who invented the bending and overblowing of notes on the instrument. Where is the continuation of 1970, when Junior Wells gave Mick Jagger a harp lesson? What is wrong with us that we leave it to the Whites to communicate the knowledge of our musical culture? It seems like we have not yet fully developed the skill to tell our own story. I have self-critical views that I would rather share in talking than in writing. And this brings me to the final point of the letter.

"I don't need the $5,000 dollars Arthur left me for the storage of the collection. I am confident I can negotiate a deal with the future owner of Arthur's house in Cairo for storing it longer than a year if need be. So I can use the money for a more immediate purpose: I would like to invite you to accompany me as my interpreter to Germany. I will try to exchange my business class ticket for two economy tickets and the $5,000 dollars should give the two of us great fourteen days in the country of your birth. If the exchange of the ticket is not possible, you can use the business class ticket and I will purchase an economy ticket. $4,000 dollars should still suffice for our trip expenses. What do you think?

"Expecting your affirmative reply and not willing to accept any excuses I remain,

Yours

James"

My knees were a little shaky. So touched was I by this expression of trust and closeness from a person I had only met eight days before. I did not hesitate a minute.

"Hello," he answered the telephone.

"It's Walter." I said with a trembling voice. "I just read your letter. Thank you."

"Are you coming along?"

"How could I not!"

"Awesome! Any time restrictions on your side?"

"I'm free. Say when."

"I'll sort everything out with the airline and call you back soon. Janice says Hi. She would like to see you again and has suggested to drive me to Chicago."

"That would be great. You can stay at my place."

"Walter?" It was her on the phone. "How was the rest of your trip?"

"Great. I'll tell you more when we meet again. It's nice to hear your voice."

"Nice to hear yours. Just wanted to say Hi. Look forward to listening to your travel stories."

"Everything's set with James. Good talking to you. See you. Bye."

"Bye, Walter! Have a good one."

I dialed Robie's number. He replied like he had been waiting for this call.

"Where have you been, buddy? I was worried. Didn't you take your old cell phone along or check your emails on the way? Your neighbor called about the Chitlin' sign. I hadn't heard the term in a long time. So, you are okay?"

"I'm just great. I have so many things to tell. I spent two days in Cairo and the rest in Mississippi. I came back wiser and more confused at the same time. I befriended an African-American family. Perhaps I will enter in a new partnership. I found an incredible harmonica collection. The guy, who inherited it, is inviting me on a trip to Germany. Let's meet tomorrow for a long lunch, if you have time. I might be leaving for about two weeks again in two or three days. And, before I forget, I know a great place for car repairs in Horn Lake, if you ever have problems. Unbeatably cheap prices—unless you believe local Chicago advertisement—and excellent workmanship."

From the increasingly uncontrolled breathing—something that must never happen to a harper, but Robie wasn't one—on the other end of the line, I sensed he doubted I was still in my right mind.

"Sorry, this may be a bit much. But, you will understand when I tell you in greater detail. So, is lunch at our club at noon tomorrow okay? After all, may I remind you that it was the email you forwarded to me ten days ago, which has produced all this? No worries, I'm still the same old fart. Listen to this before you hang up: A famous Chicago photographer who I believe had seen everything imaginable during his professional life once told me that in Circus circles "playing the harmonica" was argot for "cunnilingus." I think I have come full circle since we spoke last. I have been writing in every spare minute during my trip and the manuscript should be ready after my return from Germany."

He sighed heavily: "I'm glad. Welcome back. But is there anything else you can still think of? I mean the country is already in full swing of its election campaign. The critical assessment of our first ever African-American President is growing by the day. I believe history will judge him better than most pundits do today. They will realize that the reasons for which they are chiding him are not his fault but systemic, and will continue to give his successors terrible headaches. The Obama library and museum will come to Chicago. I doubt it will keep the city and the state of Illinois from filing bankruptcy. It's a shame. Our politicians talk shit. They are nothing but cunning lingos, if you permit the pun. More tomorrow. Let's meet in the lobby."

"You bet."

After hanging up I sorted through the rest of my normal mail and checked my email inbox. It contained mostly useless stuff that I put in the bin or clicked away without even opening it.

But there was Monika's archived message. I started typing my reply:

"Hi Monika,

"I don't know, why you chose my friend Robie as the addressee of your email nine days ago. Like myself, he is neither a person of color nor a professional harmonica player. But, in me you certainly found an interested reader: I love the Blues, am interested in your longstanding relationship with Blues players, and have made my own experiences with the Marine family and your likes.

"You have been the final trigger for a field trip, from which I just now returned, and am writing like crazy to piece together my thoughts on the German background of the harmonica and its adoption by American Blues players. Thank you for putting me under pressure!

"This morning I was googling the summer events calendars for major American cities. Blues festivals are taking place all over, which shows how vibrant the music still is. There is a large Blues scene in Chicago with great harpers like Billy Branch and Sugar Blue, but you can just as well find the music in remote places, including in Minnesota like St. Peter or New Ulm, the 'most German town in the United States.' Where there is live Blues, there is a harmonica that helps keep the Blues alive.

"I am happy that there are still two German companies providing the player community in the United States and all over the world with the instrument that has always had an outstanding appeal to Americans of all colors and creeds. At the production site of Seydel, in

Klingenthal, Blues is an indispensable item on the musical menu of the annual September festival *Mundharmonika Live*. Blues is also held in high esteem at the annual *Harmonica Masters Workshop* of Hohner in Trossingen. Both places get regular visits from some of the best players and instructors in the world who happen to live in the American Midwest.

"I am no longer worried that you and your cousins may soon be out of work. I find too much evidence on the internet that there is ample demand for solid instruction and there are plenty of offers by great harmonica teachers. These new online schools are something that I would have loved to have when I was younger.

"I wish you continued luck and always fresh good licks.

Best regards

Walter"

I reread the draft several times. Would I compromise myself? Could Monika have mischievous intentions? What was her true identity? Was I the naive victim of a clever marketing campaign?

None of this seemed relevant in the end. The email was my way to express gratitude to whoever she or he was for helping me advance in my project.

I pushed the Send button.

Monika's Blues

Monika's Blues Trail

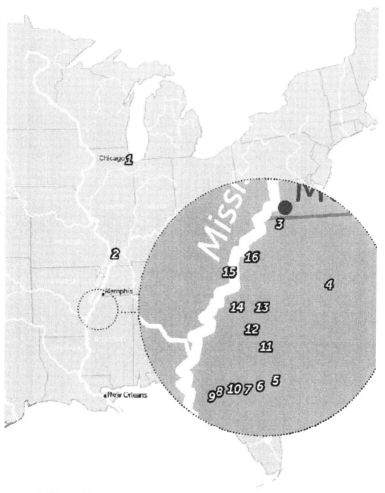

1. Chicago, IL
2. Cairo, IL
3. Horn Lake, MS
4. Oxford, MS
5. Greenwood, MS
6. Berclair, MS
7. Moorhead, MS
8. Dunleith, MS
9. Leland, MS
10. Indianola, MS
11. Glendora, MS
12. Tutwiler, MS
13. Lambert, MS
14. Clarksdale, MS
15. Helena, AR
16. Tunica, MS

Music Mentioned
(in the order of appearance)

The following songs are freely accessible online to accompany your reading.

"2120 S Michigan Ave," Rolling Stones.

"Cairo Blues," Henry Townsend.

"Midnight Creeper," James Cotton.

"Juke," Little Walter.

"Highway 49," Howlin' Wolf.

"Mean Low Blues," Blues Birdhead.

"My Babe," Little Walter.

"Walking By Myself," Jimmy Rogers.

"On the Road Again," Canned Heat.

"Luedella," Jimmy Rogers.

"Every Day I Have the Blues," B. B. King.

"The Thrill Is Gone," B. B. King.

"Hoodoo Man Blues," Buddy Guy, Junior Wells.

"Easy," Walter Horton

"Good Moanin' Blues," Walter Horton.

"Leavin' Blues," Charlie Musselwhite.

"Cross Road Blues," Robert Johnson.

"Yellow Dog Blues," W. C. Handy.

"Where the Southern Cross the Dog," Terry Evans.

"You Don't Have to Go," Jimmy Reed.

Other music Walter enjoyed on his trip, but which is not explicitly mentioned in the text.

"Don't Start Me to Talking," Sonny Boy Williamson II.

"Jackson Blues," Sonny Boy Williamson I.

"Sweet Sixteen," Junior Wells.

"Good Morning Little Schoolgirl," Sonny Boy Williamson I.

"I'm Your Hoochie Coochie Man," Muddy Waters with Little Walter.

"Sweet Home Chicago," Buddy Guy and Junior Wells.

Bibliography

Abrahamson, Terry. *In the Belly of the Blues.* Chicago: Rolling Fork Publishing, 2012.

Baugher, Shirley. *Hidden History of Old Town.* Charleston, SC: The History Press, 2011.

Berghoff, Hartmut. *Zwischen Kleinstadt und Weltmarkt, Hohner und die Harmonika 1857 – 1961.* Second Edition. Paderborn: Schöningh, 2006.

Blues Archive Poster Collection, University of Mississippi Digital Collections. clio.lib.olemiss.edu/cdm/ search/collection/bposters/ (Accessed 8 September 2016.)

Chicago Beau [Beauchamp, Jr., Lincoln T.]. *BluesSpeak.* Urbana: University of Illinois, 2010.

Chicago Beau [Beauchamp, Jr., Lincoln T.]. [Email exchange] Received by Herbert Quelle, July-September, 2015.

Chicago Beau [Beauchamp, Jr., Lincoln T.]. Personal interview. September 26, 2015.

Cohn, Lawrence. *Nothing but the Blues*. New York: Abbeville Press 1991.

Dasbach, Theo. (Rock & Blues Museum), Personal interview. July 17, 2015.

Field, Kim. *Harmonicas, Harps and Heavy Breathers*. New York: Cooper Square Press, 2000.

Filisko, Joe. "Harmonica." *Encyclopedia of the Blues.* Ed. Edward Komara. New York: Routledge, 2006.

Foster, Willie. Delta Boogie. deltaboogie.com/ deltamusicians/fosterw/. (Accessed 8 September 2016.)

George, Nelson. *The Death of Rhythm & Blues*. New York: Pantheon, 1988.

Gussow, Adam. *Mister Satan's Apprentice: A Blues Memoir*. Minneapolis: University of Minnesota Press, 2009.

Guy, Buddy and David Ritz. *When I left Home: My Story*. Boston: Da Capo Press, 2012.

Häffner, Martin and Lars Lindenmüller. *Harmonica makers of Germany and Austria: history and trademarks of Hohner and their competitors.* Trossingen: Deutsches Harmonikamuseum, 2007.

Häffner, Martin. *Auf den Spuren des Firmengründers Matthias Hohner* [*On the tracks of the company's founder Matthias Hohner*]. Second Edition. Trossingen: Deutsches Harmonikamuseum, 2013.

Häffner, Martin. *Isn't she lovely - Die Mundharmonika in der populären Musik: [erscheint als Begleitheft zur gleichnamigen Sonderausstellung des Deutschen Harmonikamuseums* (13.9. - 1.11.2009)] (Exhibition catalog). Trossingen: Harmonikamuseum Trossingen, 2009.

Häffner, Martin. *Harmonicas, Die Geschichte der Branche in Bildern und Texten.* Trossingen: Hohner Oberndorf Schwarzwälder Bote, 1991.

Handy W.C. and Arna Bontemps. *Father of the Blues.* New York: Da Capo Press, 1991 [1941].

Harmonica Project Collection (MUM00201). purl.oclc.org/umarchives/MUM00201/. (Accessed 8 September 2016.)

Hoffman, Mark and James Segrest. *Moanin' at Midnight, The Life and Times of Howlin' Wolf.* New York: Pantheon Books, 2004.

Johnson, Greg and Edward Komara. *100 books every Blues fan should own.* Lanham, MD: Rowman &

Littlefield, 2014.

Kauert, Kurt. *Der Musikwinkel und die Harmonika*. Marienberg: Druck- und Verlagsgesellschaft, 2000.

Koester, Bob. Personal interview. February 23, 2015.

Lämmle, August. *Matthias Hohner. Leben und Werk des Musikinstrumentenherstellers in Trossingen.* Stuttgart: Cotta, 1957.

LeRoi Jones (Baraka, Amiri). *Black Music.* New York: Akashic Books, 2010.

LeRoi Jones (Baraka, Amiri). *Blues people: Negro music in White America.* New York : Harper Perennial, 2002.

Licht, Michael S. "Harmonica Magic: Virtuoso Display in American Folk Music." *Ethnomusicology.* Vol. 24, No. 2 (May, 1980), pp. 211-221.

"Little Hatchet Band ~ "S/T" (M & M) Germany 1974 rare album! + 4 page insert!" (Provine Hatch). CollectorsFrenzy. Collectorsfrenzy.com/details/270874529095/little_hatchet_band __st_m__m_Germany_1974_rare_album __4_page_insert. (Accessed 8 September 2016.)

Lornell, Kip. *Virginia's Blues, Country, and Gospel Records, 1902 – 1943: an annotated discography.* Lexington, KY: University Press of Kentucky,

1989.

Marina Bokelman Collection (MUM00584). purl.oclc.org/umarchives/MUM00584/ (Accessed 8 September 2016.)

Martin Feldmann Collection (MUM00456). purl.oclc.org/umarchives/MUM00456/. (Accessed 8 September 2016.)

Oliver, Paul and Max Harrison. *The New Grove gospel, blues, and jazz, with spirituals and ragtime.* New York: W.W. Norton & Company, 1986.

Palmer, Robert. *Deep Blues: A Musical and Cultural History from the Mississippi Delta to Chicago's South Side to the World.* New York: Penguin Books, 1982.

Peabody, Charles. "Notes on Negro Music." *The Journal of American Folklore.* Vol. 16, No. 62 (Jul. - Sep., 1903), pp. 148-152. http://www.jstor.org/stable/533498 (accessed July 12, 2015)

Pöllman, Werner. *Einblicke in 650 Jahre Stadtentwicklung Nothaft im Egerland, Neukirchen im Vogtland, Markneukirchen in Sachsen. Hauptsitz des Orchesterinstrumentenbaus in Deutschland ; [2010 - 1360 - 1274 ; 650 jähriges Stadtjubiläum].* Markneukirchen: Markneukirchen Stadtverwaltung, 2010.

Red Saunders Research Foundation. www.redsaunders .com. Accessed 8 September 2016.

Reich, Howard. *Let Freedom Swing: Collected Writings on Jazz, Blues, and Gospel.* Evanston: Northwestern University Press, 2010.

Restle, Conny. „*In aller Munde"* : *Mundharmonika, Handharmonika, Harmonium, eine 200-jährige Erfolgsgeschichte; [anlässlich der Ausstellung „In aller Munde" im Musikinstrumenten-Museum SIMPK, Berlin, 2. Oktober bis 17. November 2002].* Berlin: Musikinstrumenten-Museum, 2002.

"Revisiting Cairo, Illinois." abandonedonline.net. (Accessed 8 September 2016.)

Rowe, Mike. *Chicago Blues: the City [and] the Music.* New York: Da Capo Press, 1988.

Samuelson, Tim (Chicago city historian). Personal interview. December 11, 2015.

Shadwick, Keith. *Blues: Keeping the Faith.* Edison, NJ: Chartwell Books, 1998.

Sharp, Tim. *Memphis Music: Before the Blues.* Charleston, SC: Arcadia Publishing, 2007.

Shatkin, Bob Collection (MUM01756). purl.oclc.org/ umarchives/MUM01756/ (Accessed 8 September 2016.)

Sheldon Harris Collection MUM00682. purl.oclc.org/ umarchives/MUM00682/ (Accessed 8 September 2016.)

Steinbeck, John. *The Grapes of Wrath* [et al]. Minneapolis: Amaranth Press, MN, 1984.

Stolle, Roger. (Cat Head). Personal interview. July 17, 2015.

Stolle, Roger and Lou Bopp. *Hidden History of the Mississippi Blues*. Charleston, SC: The History Press, 2011.

Trynka, Paul and Valerie Wilmer. *Portrait of the Blues.* New York: Da Capo Press, 1997.

Wagner, Christoph. *Die Mundharmonika: Ein musikalischer Globetrotter*. Berlin: Transit, 1996.

Wardlow, Gayle and Edward M Komara. *Chasin' that Devil Music: Searching for the Blues.* San Francisco: Miller Freeman Books, 1998.

Wenzel, Haik and Martin Häffner. *Legende Hohner Harmonika: Mundharmonika und Akkordeon in der Welt der Musik [Hohner, the living legend: harmonicas and accordions around the world]*. Bergkirchen: PPVMedien, Edition Bochinsky, 2006.

Whiteis, David. *Chicago Blues, Portraits and Stories*. Urbana, IL: University of Illinois, 2006.

www.Patmissin.com. www.patmissin.com/. Accessed 8
    September 2016.

Yerxa, Winslow. *Blues Harmonica for Dummies.* Hobo-
    ken, NJ: John Wiley & Sons, 2012.

About the Author

Herbert Quelle is a career diplomat who currently serves as the Consul General of the Federal Republic of Germany in Chicago. He joined the German Foreign Service in 1980 and has had assignments abroad in Los Angeles, Pretoria, Havana, Warsaw, London, Baku and Boston before moving to Chicago in 2014.

Mr. Quelle is an amateur musician, composer and writer.

He is married and has two children.

Monika's Blues